GOLD IS WHERE

YOU FIND IT

by

Albert A. Jones

651392

VANTAGE PRESS

New York / Washington / Atlanta / Hollywood

GOLD IS WHERE YOU FIND IT

This blacksmith had confided a great many items of his past to me over the years. It was always a puzzle to me why he did so but I had listening ears and a retentive memory. We seemed on good terms and often he had some interesting new story for me. In the days after Roosevelt had raised the price of gold to $35 an ounce his mind went back to a time many years before when he had quit stage driving to wash gold himself. "Jones," he said, "are you interested in gold and the getting of it? Would you care to hear of a little adventure of mine?"

"Why, yes, Mr. Ephraim, that would interest me greatly. If you can spare the time, I am free on this particular Saturday afternoon and so please tell me about it. I know you grew up in Oregon and drove stage at an early age, but a gold miner —that is news to me. Please go on." So Mr. Ephraim began telling of his adventures of many years before. . . .

There had been news of a strike in the dry area of Oregon, so I went on horseback in that direction but got caught away from water and had to spend a night in the desert. However, the saddle horse and the packhorse and I did get to water the next day. We made it to camp and got a claim of our own and I made the gravel fly. There was gold in that sandstone and soon a public retort room was set up. There, we miners would refine the gold from the amalgam ourselves. The amalgam was formed in our sluices by mercury absorbing the fine gold dust. In the retort this amalgam became heated and the mercury passed up as a vapor. This vapor passed into tubes in water and so became cooled, and we thus saved our mercury to be used the next day. No matter how careful we were some of that vapor would escape into the air; we would hang damp cloths before our faces to keep from breathing it. Mercury is very detrimental to the health of any animal. A man could sometimes wring mercury from those cloths after a retort session. There was a waiting room where we miners could be comfortable while awaiting our turns at the retort.

In the retort room, we often found compatible men; indeed, one man in particular became my friend and we shared the same tent while I was in that camp. That is the way life is. As we journey along, a certain comradeship develops between people who are compatible. Why, I do not know. But David LaFollette had a rare quality that made us feel friends. He was much older than I was but we hit it off from the first, and his memory stays with me.

One night he seemed talkative and discoursed on the way gold is deposited. "Now Hinton," he said, "your name, I believe you told me, is Hinton T. Ephraim. That is a name to be proud of. I knew your father and a fine blacksmith he was. This gold vein here is, as you know, sandstone, and it stretches through the country on edge. Not flat but nearly vertical. We know that sandstone was once a bed of sand and was deposited mostly under water and so would be nearly flat, as you see the sandbeds in the streams nowadays. The gold was washed from higher ground and carried in past times along with the sand and left to settle. This sandbed in time was most likely covered up with dirt or volcanic eruption, as it is in Inyo County, California. In the course of years the sandbed compacted and became what we call sandstone. This in our claims is really not yet hard stone because we can dig it out easily with picks. But at some point the convulsions of the earth broke this particular vein from the bed and set it up on edge. We came here after some curious prospector found it and we

2

are getting gold from it. Where the remainder of the original sandbed is or where the source of the gold is, is not known. We do not need to know it. Our part is to take care to make use of our good fortune and get the gold that God put here for our use."

"That is very interesting, Mr. LaFollette, I am now very glad I came here, even though there was that dry camp I had to make. But now I am prospering."

He grinned and then said, "I must tell you about the time I got caught on the desert in Nevada. But to really understand about it you should hear the story of how I got there. Do you want to hear the story of that time in 1850?" He continued. "I was born in a log cabin near New Albany, Indiana. I grew up there and married and by 1850 had my wife and children on a farm in Jasper County, Iowa. But the stories of the rich gold strikes in California got me anxious to go and get my share. So leaving them on the farm and joining a group of friends, I took off.

"We were twelve, each with a good horse and saddle bags filled with what we thought must be needed. Most of us grew up among the Baptists and most of us were Washingtonians. That was a group of people who were total abstainers from alcoholic beverages. But I had a quart of vinegar and a quart of honey and some dried sassafras bark and dried comfrey leaves for tea. My people had learned to keep in good health and maintain their strength by using the common wisdom which our ancestors handed down for hundreds of years. We knew that the Rechebites and Nazarites of Bible records were total abstainers also, but we took the name of Washingtonians in honor of George Washington who abhorred drunkenness and advised against it.

"We made good progress across Iowa, Nebraska and well into Wyoming. Many individuals and many wagon trains followed the same route. Our bunch kept close together but we sometimes had keen discussions about the current topics: slavery, the hope for wagon roads. Some even expressed the thought that railroads would some day push far west—even to

California. It seemed to most of us only a dream.

"Edward King seemed to be dubious about my beliefs. 'Do you,' he asked, 'do you really believe that you were pre-destined to go after gold. And that you would be with this group. And that you will live to gain a fortune. And that you will get back home to your family?'

" 'Yes, Ed,' I replied, 'that is my belief. My trust is in the Almighty who will direct my path and lead me to a fortune and guide me to my home again. You must believe likewise or else why are you here?'

"John Anderson joined in and said, 'Ed and I are indeed hoping for all these good things for ourselves. And for all of this group. We do trust the Almighty but we do not know that all our hopes will be realized. Do you?'

" 'John, my belief is strong that certainly all the above stated objects will be attained. I am as sure of it as I am that we shall see the sun tomorrow.'

" 'If so,' said Edward, 'then why do you take your two teaspoons of vinegar and two teaspoonsful of honey each week. You are certain of the outcome, so why bother?'

"I replied, 'Now that is just it. God taught our ancestors how to keep well, and me also. I am predestined to use these aids to health and I will if possible.'

"There came a time when we camped near a big ren-dezvous where traders gathered to bargain with trappers for beaver and buffalo pelts. There were goods for the trappers to last them till the next year. And there was whiskey also; many trappers drank too much.

"Half of us stayed in camp a short distance from the gathering. The others went in to observe the ways of those rugged pioneers. That evening Edward King returned to tell us about one man who had completely passed out. 'Now, David, you said that vinegar and honey drink will bring such a one out of his hangover. Will you try it?'

" 'Certainly, I will try. Bring him out here and see that we have plenty of water and quiet.'

"So they carried him to me and Ben Ferrin helped me by

holding up his head as he sat there. I had the drink ready and found he could not drink. We managed to use a teaspoon to get a few drops into his mouth. It took us an hour to get a cupful into him. Then in three more hours we tried again. The third time he could drink some. We kept this up at three-hour intervals all night. By morning he was much better and by night almost recovered. He could sleep then, and early in the second day we started again on the three-hour treatment. He felt well enough to talk and told us someone had drugged his drink.

"His name was Etienne Ronald and he had grown up in St. Louis but had been on the plains trapping beaver and hunting many years. He thanked us and went back to the big camp. But he had told me some things about his life and claimed he was not a drunkard. I asked him if he did not spend many months each year on the lonely plains and during that time feel well and strong. Then why drink whiskey when in the big camp? If you leave booze alone, wouldn't you feel good all the time?

"We stayed there a while resting and trying to learn the best way to go on to the gold fields, and early one morning in came Etienne Ronald to tell us there was a fine herd of buffalo a few miles away. He said we should go out there and kill a few head and make jerky in the hot dry time. This jerky would travel well in our saddlebags. . .and prove a great aid to us, as we might not find game all along the way. He would show us the herd and help us dry the meat.

"We decided to break camp and go over to the herd and try our luck. He took us to where the herd was and beyond to a nice spot for a camp with water. We got settled and left our saddlebags and managed to kill four giant buffaloes. Etienne showed us how to skin and cut up the meat so as to bring it to camp. We set to the job of cutting the meat into strips and laid it on poles to dry in the hot sun. We had a fine feast on liver and heart. This was a change from bacon.

"The next day several Indians visited our camp. We could not talk with them but offered them some of the meat to eat. Etienne talked to them and told us they wished us to kill some of the buffalo for them. He said we should make a deal. If we killed eight buffalo they would let us have four ponies. We would need them to pack the jerky.

"Well, that turned out all right. We managed to kill eight for them and they turned over four ponies to us. Etienne stayed with us and he took an especial interest in me. He told me many things about his life. He had found good Indians and the other kind also. Once he had to hide out from enemies for two weeks. They even watched the water holes. He told me that a man could take a lobe of prickly pear cactus and pare off the outside with the spines and eat the pithy juicy inner part for water and nourishment. He said to watch what the animals ate as an indication of what was fit to eat in case of necessity.

"So in a few days the jerky was ready and we were ready and we said our goodbyes to Etienne, who went back to the big camp.

"We passed out of Wyoming, through what is now Utah, and into Nevada. Then calamity struck. I had been sampling different plants the horses ate and fell desperately ill. I could not ride or walk. Also, we had missed the spring we expected to find. The men stayed with me all night and the next morning I told them that they should go on.

" 'I want only my saddlebags and empty canteens. You must take my horse. If not he will die. I do not expect to die but you will if you stay. Why should you and the horses perish because I am sick. If I recover, which I think likely, some other party might come along and take me with them. Your duty now is to go on, find a spring, and save yourselves and the horses.'

"They finally went on and I lay in the shade of a small bush using my blanket to shade me from the sun. Perhaps my stomach was not as strong as the horses' were. I remembered when our dog, Spot, got sick, he would not eat but lay quietly munching on grass. In time, he became well and strong again. I found some cactus and whittled a sharp stick and stuck it into

6

a lobe of the cactus. With my jackknife I pared the spines away and chewed on the inner part. That helped a little. Next morning I could crawl a little and got to a small rise and looked about me.

"A short distance away there appeared to be some green trees. That might mean water was at their roots. Could I get there? Well, I could surely try. Before the sun was up I was looking down into a canyon where trees grew. By careful crawling and even some sliding, I got to the bottom. No water. There was mud and on all sides were dead animals that had come to find water where there was none. And so they had perished, as I would if God did not direct me to water.

"But I did note that the mud was moist. I had brought my canteen and a cup and decided that by digging I might find water. We did that in Indiana one dry summer. Well, with the cup and knife, I got to scraping the mud away. And yes, not too far down there was water. With thanks to God I got a small basin laid bare and let the water settle. Took a cupful and let it settle. Then a sip and a little later another sip. Thus I got a small cupful into my system and began to feel better. Then, looking about me, I spied some green grass that had grown after the last horse had died. A little bite of green grass and then some more of the water, which was now well settled. I crawled to the shade of a big tree and rested awhile. Then I sat up and looked around. There was a horse that seemed not to have been dead long. I went over to it and cut off some lean meat. It appeared to be good, so I got a fire started and broiled a slice on a stick. It tasted good. I broiled the whole chunk but ate only a small part of it to begin with. More water. More green growth. Then rest in the shade. I stayed down there all night. Early in the morning I got the canteen partially full of water and took some cooked meat and crawled up to the top.

"I rested a while after I got over to the shady bush. Then I got out the remains of the vinegar and honey and mixed a half cup of water with four teaspoonfuls. That hit the spot. There was a little jerky too, and I chewed on that all day up

7

there and I even made some sassafras tea with a little comfrey in it. That was very good. I felt better by the minute. Back down for the night. So it went. I would spend the night down there and crawl up to my saddlebags for the day. I remembered how Etienne had counseled that we choose a captain. We had picked George Bunche to be captain. He was a good man and a good captain. I hoped the men had gotten through to water. I thought about my wife and babies on the farm in Iowa. Would they keep going alone? We had agreed that if I did not get back there by October 15, she should write home to have brother John come to get the crops in and the wood cut and see them through the winter.

"One morning I could even stand without being dizzy. I looked to the East. There was a party of horsemen. I waved and shot off my revolver—three well-spaced shots. They veered over my way. That resulted in a pleasant surprise.

"The leader was Etienne Ronald. They listened while I spoke of my sickness and then asked if they would take me with them. Etienne had taken the task of guiding this party of six to California. He had decided the beaver were nearly all caught. Perhaps he should try washing gold himself. They agreed to pay him three hundred dollars to guide them. That was very fortunate for me.

"Etienne said they had a spare horse since they had consumed part of the supplies. 'Do you think you can ride a horse?' he asked.

" 'I believe I can if you will help me get on its back.'

"We got my saddlebags together. Then I thought about the water situation. I told them there was a little water in that canyon but Etienne said not to worry about that tiny bit. There was a good water hole an hour's ride from that spot. So off we went. The water was there. But Bunche and the others had not found it. It was many months before I learned how they had prospered. Meantime, we were getting along toward California—and riches, we hoped.

"The desert was reaching toward the mountains. We journeyed nearer these rising masses that loomed between us and our hoped-for gold hoards. We were able to get some fresh meat to go with our jerky. We met no other groups, nor indeed were we able to find a trace of my former comrades. We were glad that we found no dead men or horses; we judged that they had gotten over the mountains safely.

"Then, in the higher reaches of the mountains, there were giant trees such as we had not seen. At last we were over the crest and following streams we knew led toward the Pacific. The horse I rode was getting tired so we took counsel and decided I should stop and rest the pony. Etienne went on with the men who had hired him. In four days he returned to find me well rested and the pony almost frisky. He had received his three hundred dollars, as his men considered his task finished.

"He told me that from what he had been told by old friends about the gold gravels there was a good chance we could veer off to the south of the trail the group followed and find our own private diggings. He had a second pony, so we now had three horses. After resting another day, we went on our way hoping to get down to a good stream with clean gravel bars where gold should be. He reasoned that in the headwaters we might well find coarser gold that gathered up there while the finer dust had been washed down nearer Sutter's Fort.

"We took our time and in a few days came down a slope into a valley where a good-sized stream had left a nice bar. After making camp we took our gold pans and tried our hand. He showed me how to swirl the water and gravel in the pan. Yes, there were the glittering particles. So we decided to make camp on the nearby open meadow and spend a few months washing the precious metal. It would take us green hands several months to work out the gold from that bar. Each of us had a gold pan. Each of us had a rifle and a revolver. The skies were clear, the river was low. We worked at washing gold in our clumsy fashion for several days. The toil was rewarding. We did not fear any other parties would pass near us, for we were careful to hide our trail on the way down.

"Feeling safe, Etienne and I called a temporary halt to

our prospecting activities. He went after deer. I laid out an orderly camp. The next day back he came with two fine bucks. Then we both set at making jerky. We scraped together ashes from our campfire and in a pit set the hides to soaking in ashes and water to loosen the hair.

"While at these tasks, we decided to build a good cabin in case our labors should keep us there into winter. I had my keen-bladed axe and a froe and a brace and bit. Also a good whetstone. We cut down nice, smooth straight trees about six or eight inches through for the walls of the cabin. We would wash gold a few hours each day, then we went at the logs. Of course, the axe work was tiring, but we got enough logs ready and we carried several large flat rocks to the cabin site to serve as a foundation. The cabin was only ten feet by twelve feet, but we wanted it snug and solid. Etienne was good at cutting notches at the ends. When we laid up the logs, the notches were such that their own weight held them in place.

"We found a fine straight-grained tree and made shakes. That is where the froe proved a great help. We had our door in one end toward the East. A fireplace in the north side. The brace and bit came in handy to bore holes in the logs at the door and fireplace openings. That way we could fasten the ends of the logs in place by wooden pins. I was born in a log cabin put together with wooden pins for lack of iron nails, so I could build after that fashion.

"We built the gables off-center so that eight-foot shakes were long enough for the north side of the roof but would project out on the south side for a sort of a shed. We had got a good tree so that we could make as many eight-foot shakes as we needed. In time the walls were up. The shakes on the roof were pinned with wooden pins and we took time out to build the fireplace. The door was of shakes also.

"Some rock salt from my pack kept the horses from straying far away from camp. We laid up some large rocks for an outdoor fire to cook while the weather remained good, which it did for several months.

"When we could slip the hair from the deerskins then

came the task of tanning. We found some bark to use in pits to do the tanning and Etienne went and got two more deer, so we had brains to aid in that process. The softer parts on the belly were for gold pouches, for which we thought we would have need. The leather from the backs were suitable for moccasins. My pal Etienne was a good maker of moccasins and in time he taught me the craft.

"Well, we tanned hides. We made pouches. We filled several of those pouches to our great joy. We finally got the fireplace laid up with sticks daubed with some clay from a deposit nearby. Then we worked more steadily at washing out the gold. Late in October we saw our supply of flour and salt was apt to be used up, so after consideration, Etienne took the horses and some gold and went off to locate a trading post and try to bargain for enough to keep us while we got the rest of the bar worked over.

"I kept at the washing and waited for his return. We had thought he might be fortunate enough to be back in two weeks, but no such luck. Not in three weeks, or in four weeks. But before the fifth week ended, he came. He had a nice supply of goods and a story to tell.

"He had found a trading post. Mr. Richfield, the owner, had set up shop among the mining claims along a main tributary of the Sacramento River. He did not have all the articles ,we wanted but thought that a shipment was about due at Docktown. Would Etienne take the horses and pack it up? Well, if Richfield would send a man along, he would make the trip for two hundred dollars. So the bargain was struck and that was why it took so long to get back to our snug cabin. And our needs were met.

"I had been washing gold, tanning deerskins, and checking over the cabin to be sure that all was in good tight order. Now we both set to with great resolve and made the gravel fly. Things turned out as Etienne had predicted. Our gold ran much coarser than that near the trading post, which in turn was not as fine as that near Docktown. Miners were feverishly getting out the gold. Prices were high. Food was scarce. Etienne had killed two fine bucks going down and sold most of the venison for fabulous prices. He thought no one would be able to track him back to our camp. That made us feel easy. Perhaps in our haste we did not save all the finer dust, but we were filling more pouches as the days passed.

"We found ripe berries in the woods and took time off from mining to get a few grouse in the woods. There were some wild 'miner's lettuce' to be had in the vicinity. We were getting quite comfortable in our finished cabin, with its well-daubed fireplace. We made two bunks in the back end and did not fear the approach of winter. But Etienne cautioned me about the shorter and cooler days. If a deep snow came overnight what would the horses do? We had worked most of the bar for gold and thought we each had near eight thousand dollars worth. Why take chances? We wanted to get down to the lower valley and see how other miners did. I had given much thought to my family, but they had decided what to do in case my return was delayed. I had now done well and thought another year among the miners might well prove worthwhile.

"So we snugged up the cabin and gathered a store of dry firewood in case we should return. Then we packed our saddlebags and the pack saddle and set out. Etienne was a past master at concealing a trail, so we felt certain no one would track ours to the cabin. What if they did? We had gotten the gold, or at least most of it.

"We took our time and looked about us at the fine forests along the high ridges, which is where we rode for the most part. We even passed through some snow before getting to Mr. Richfield's trading post. There were claims all about and miners busily washing out that golden treasure. George Richfield was a fine sociable man, but worried about supplies. He made an offer to Etienne Ronald to make another trip to pack in more goods from Docktown. So by January 1, 1851, we bought another pony and went on down the valley.

"The trail to Docktown was now beginning to be traveled. We met miners with packhorses and with packs on their backs coming up from Docktown. Down there the weather was mild and scarcely any rain fell in four days. We reached the warehouse and took stock of the prospects. At the bank we turned in our dust and I sent a thousand dollars to my wife in Jasper County, Iowa. We found good grazing on the corner of Mr. Jake Stone's claims and, as we had brought him some fresh venison, we were given permission to camp there. We rested a day and then took off with full packs for George Richfield's trading post."

Mr. Ephraim yawned and said, "Jones, this is getting to be a long story and I am getting tired. Perhaps you are not interested in this account of the doings in the gold mines of 1850, but I found it very interesting when my friend told it to me and most of the details still interest me. How about you? If you wish to hear the rest I will be glad to go on, but let us put it off for two weeks. Next Saturday I am pledged to help test some mine prospects, but two weeks from now we could try to get this story ended."

It didn't take long for me to answer him. "Yes, Mr. E-phraim," I replied, "I am keenly interested. The story of how those pioneers worked and prospered excites me. Let us meet in two weeks and continue with the next chapter."

The above tale, as related by Mr. Ephraim, was the fuller story of my great uncle. My grandfather, his younger brother, wrote the whole outline in the geneaology of their family, which I have seen and read. Also, my Uncle Jerry told me of the way the family in Iowa got along during that winter of 1850-51. In those far-off times, the Primitive Predestinarian Baptists were a close-knit order, and their families came together to offer each other mutual aid. So when Grandfather got a letter from his sister-in-law in October 1850 requesting him to come from Indiana to help them get in the crops and wood and see them safely through the winter, he was certain that it was foreordained by the Almighty that he should make the journey and do his part. He believed that the whole situation was foreordained. And, indeed, Great Uncle David and his wife had agreed she should write such a letter if he had not returned by that time. I myself saw that letter. Therefore, brother John got ready and started on horseback from Indiana, where his father had a fine farm and was a famous breeder of horses and cattle. John LaFollette went on his way from Indiana, across Southern Illinois, to Ottunwa, Iowa. Before leaving on the journey, his horse seemed travel-weary and he decided to trade for a fresh mount. A fine black stallion took his fancy. A kind onlooker advised him not to buy that one, saying that horse was fractious and would likely cause his death. But John had grown up with the best horses and thought himself well able to handle any horse. So he made the deal and started on his way. He spent the night in western Wapello County, Iowa, where there was a sleet storm. In the morning he started out in the chill air and the stallion proved obstreperous. In the end he slipped and fell on the rider's leg, breaking it.

This took place near the house of the Easley family, who saw the whole affair. The father and sons, Bill and Joe, came out and took control of the horse and helped John to the house. They sent for Dr. Gutch, who came out from Blakesburg and set the bone. The doctor drove a one-horse buggy drawn by a fine sleek young mare. Dr. Gutch advised bed rest and said he would return in a few days. The Easleys made him welcome. They put the stallion in the big stable by himself and then they went out into the fields to cut and shock corn. They were close-order Baptists, too, and the daughter and mother and sisters were like the women of most farm families in those times—well trained in the tasks fit for them. That is to say, Angeline knew how to care for livestock. She knew how to wash and comb wool and spin it into yarn, to weave it into homespun cloth. The family grew flax and she could take her part in retting it. She could break it and comb the fibers and spin them into thread to be woven into linen.

When that strong young man was lying under the horse, she wondered if it was foreordained that he should come into the home and meet her in that way. She liked his appearance.

14

She was not yet fifteen, but if it was foreordained that they should meet and he might fall in love with her—well, then she was in favor of foreordination. Of course, he must lie or at least sit with his leg in a cast, but he could hold the tow while she spun it into thread or wind the yarn which she spun. The men contrived a rough crutch, so in a day or two he could hobble about. When Dr. Gutch came with his mare, Dove, to check the broken leg, there was John hobbling with his crutch.

He said, "Dr. Gutch, that mare seems nubile. I believe she knows that stallion, Nig, is in the barn. Why don't you unharness her and take her into the barn and see what comes of it." The doctor looked in the barn and saw that fine stallion and thought well of it, so he took Dove in there and closed the doors.

Now Angeline saw this. Having grown up among horses and cattle, she knew what it was about. She heard various snorts and noises and was certain of the success of the affair. She hoped Dove would have a fine colt. The day that Nig fell on John, she knew he was a good judge of horseflesh. This day, she was certain he was a good businessman. She heard Dr. Gutch say, "If Dove has a fine colt, that will be pay for what I have done for your broken leg."

As time passed, John took more exercise. His leg healed and was in good shape. The men took counsel with him and told him they had five mares. The only good stallion had been taken on to Albia and would not be back. Could they turn them in with Nig as each came in heat? "Fine," John said. So in turn Brownie, Spot, Maud, Blackie and Fluff were ushered into the barn. John improved to the point that Dr. Gutch said he might ride a bit if he were careful. In another week he felt able to continue the journey. Farewells were said and he went on toward the North. He stopped overnight at a farmhouse. The people had mares. Some were ready, so Nig did his part and John took in fees. Three different times he laid over a day for this. At last he got to the farm and found his sister-in-law and the three youngsters thriving. He set to getting the corn cut and the potatoes dug. The pumpkins, squash, cabbage, carrots, and turnips all came in for careful harvest and storage. Of course, they all pitched in and helped. Those close-order Baptists were able to work and expected to work. They believed it was foreordained that they should work and also foreordained that they prosper. John chopped and hauled great piles of wood, for the winters in northern Iowa could be severe and the fireplace would need much stoking. As he became acquainted with the local populace, he found opportunities to take in many dollars as fees for Nig's services. He decided his choice had been a wise one and took off one day fifteen miles in one direction, and next week fifteen miles in another direction, so that his cash fund built up steadily.

Then in March came the $1,000 draft from David. They were all glad to know he had prospered and set about the spring work with a glad heart. Later a letter came to let them know he would stay another year in California and would send money to them.

So John stayed with the family and put in the crops and cared for the stock. Three mares had colts and John continued his regular circuits in adjoining townships. Nig took the fancy of the local farmers; indeed he was a fine stallion. John knew horseflesh. The summer of 1851 was a busy time, and if the farm crops brought low prices those bank drafts came at intervals from California. They spent money only on what was needed and laid by the greater part of their revenues.

Summer—get in the hay; fall—cut great piles of wood and cut and shock the corn. And, of course, in November, dig the potatoes and carrots and turnips and so forth and store them for food and fodder. In winter, feed the fires and shuck out the corn, prepare and grain fodder for stock feed and grain for corn bread and cornmeal mush. They had many uses for corn. Of course, the flax was carefully handled to make linen cloth and the sheep sheared in spring for wool for the yarn to knit and weave into warm cloth.

So the months passed and the spring of 1852 came on apace. On his circuits with Nig our John had got perhaps 25 miles south of the farm. Here in early March David arrived,

16

having come up from Keokuk, Iowa. Encountering John here, they had a good talk and the next day both made it up to the farm. The children had grown and almost forgotten their father, but their mother rejoiced to see him. After many hearty embraces, the children forgot their timidity and listened closely to the story the wanderer had to tell of his travels. He had come home in good health and with a fortune of nearly $70,000. This was mostly deposited in banks in St. Louis.

David had decided to sell the farm and take the family back to New Albany. They were to be well ensconced in a good farmhouse near their kinfolk and he proposed to take another trip to California that spring. No time was to be lost. They found a buyer for the farm and stock; David kept only a good team and covered wagon. The terms were $5,000 down and $5,000 in two years. In two weeks they were on their way. John rode Nig. David gave him $1,000; in addition, John had saved $1,200 from his work with Nig.

In three days' travel they reached the Easley home and stopped off for two days. Angeline was glad to see John and he was glad to see her. It didn't take them long to make up their minds; they married almost at once. Her first child was born before she was fifteen years old. They became wealthy on the farm and reared a large family. John later traveled into Indiana, Missouri, even as far west as western Oregon. There he visited David. He wrote a book giving the history of the family from 1745 on. He was my grandfather and I have given this record partly from that book he published and partly from what Mother's brother, my Uncle Jerry, told and showed me.

Back to Hinton T. Ephraim. Two Saturday afternoons later we were together again. He went on recounting the words of David LaFollette.

"The trip upriver with heavy-loaded packhorses was begun. We had gotten a fourth horse and the goods made full loads for them all. Etienne and I walked and it took us five days to get back to the trading post. Our wages were six

17

hundred dollars. Then Mr. Richfield begged us to take on the job of bringing up his goods from Docktown on a steady basis. We wished to remain in the valley and see if we could get onto the track of our one-time traveling companions. This seemed a good way to earn good wages and, perhaps, we could also meet up with some of our old colleagues. If he gave us eight hundred dollars for a round trip we would take on the task. So off we went, taking some parcels down with us. Miners sent gold pouches to the bank. We got enough that way to take care of our cash outlay.

"We took time off to get a couple more deer and at Docktown had ready sale for what we could spare. Of course, George Stone got part of it. The next day he talked with us about his problem.

"There were two giant trees on part of the claim, besides other smaller ones. He wished to get those big trees removed, for he planned a ditch to carry water to a sluice for washing gold. Did we know anyone who would get them out? We looked over the job and said if he gave us two hundred dollars we would take them out. Richfield's goods had not come as yet. We had our axes and I got a file and a saw from the dockmaster at a cost of fifty dollars. The trees leaned slightly and we dug at the base cutting away the roots as we went down. We dug a trench four feet wide and kept at it until it was three-quarters the way around and five feet deep. Then we cut off the tap roots at the bottom so that we had cut back under the tree. Then we went over to the other side and began cutting the roots there that still held the tree upright. Digging and cutting we finally got most of the roots cut on that side. At last the two big roots we had purposely left for last were about all that held the tree in place. We got our axes well sharpened and began chopping at those roots. When they were cut off the tree toppled, tearing out with its great weight the few roots remaining uncut. That was a nice piece of work. Then we went at the next tree. We were allowed two weeks to get those trees out and they were down in one week. We were to have the wood.

"It remained for us to cut up the trunks and tops into small enough pieces to be able to move them. Here the cross-cut saw paid for itself. We cut the stump with four feet of trunk off. Then we cut two eight-foot logs from each tree. Then we cut up the upper parts where the limbs were. We had permission to take the entire trees. Stone wanted them out of his way. We sold some for wood and with the horses' aid cleared the way for the ditch. Stone was surprised and pleased. He readily paid us the two hundred dollars and agreed we might build a cabin in a barren corner of his claim.

"There were no limbs or knots in the lower twenty feet of those trees. With gluts we split those giant logs and made them fit to rive into shakes with my froe. They rived into nice eight-foot shakes. But just as we started at that job, here came Mr. Richfield's goods.

"So off we went with our horses well-laden. Mr. Richfield had become almost frantic but could not blame us for the boats' delay. We had some pelts and gold to take down but there was no freight. So we rived the four big logs into shakes and built and eight-by-twelve-foot cabin. We put it together with wooden pins, as we had done before upriver. It was a pleasant feeling to have a roof over our heads. We had lots of shakes left and made a shelter for the horses also. Another shipment for Mr. Richfield sent us up with our pack train. Coming back with only light loads, we took time to detour and bring two deer carcasses down. We sold most of them. The captain of the freight boat bought some and while on board I spied a wimble and borrowed it while he laid by a few days. I had an idea.

"We went up the slope of the mountain and found two trees about eight inches through. On the side hill the trees curved at the bottom. We cut them off at the lower part of the curve. They were like sled runners, and that is exactly what we made of them. We hewed them neatly and drug them down by the cabin. We used the wimble to bore a set of holes to make an elongated hole in each at a place near the end. We made a crosspiece of good timber and shaped the ends with

19

shoulders and a tongue which we put through the sled runners. Then we split the protruding ends and drove wedges into them so as to keep the runners rigid. After putting shakes on the crosspieces, we had a sled.

"Using castoff ropes and chains from the ships, we rigged harnesses and deerskin for breast straps and put together a four-horse team. We used an old anchor chain in place of a tongue, and now we believed we could use the horses to drag a thousand-pound load up the trail. We took the team out on a few practice runs and then another lot of goods came and we subjected our sled to a trial. By handling the horses carefully, we could get along the trail better than with the pack train. On the farm where I grew up we called such a rig a stoneboat and found it very useful. As we went upriver, there was a three-inch snowstorm and our sled really went along well. Back again and waiting for a load, another bright idea blossomed forth.

"We took our crosscut saw and carefully sawed four blocks off the tough stumps. We took great care to saw a true cut. Then, with the ship's wimble we made holes in the center of each. These holes were five inches across. Then I made axles to pierce at each end through the blocks. So we had wheels for a rough wagon. We made those holes smooth and used bear grease to stop the squeaking. Now a body was placed on the axles and we could haul a ton of goods. The snow had melted and the sled was not so useful.

"Well, that Mr. Richfield was a surprised man. But pleased also. And we were pleased. The trail was becoming smoothed and straightened under the constant travel of horses and men, and we made good progress back down. We drug a log down for a brake. We made the down trip one day short but late. So we slept in. But no soap. At daylight there was a racket and a pounding and a man called out, 'Arise and shine. You will never get rich lying in bed. Come forth and greet the dawn!'

"Well, we crawled out and there were two of our old trailmates. They said they had heard at the dock that a man named Etienne Ronald and a man named David lived in this cabin and they came over to talk about old times. I sure was surprised and pleased.

" 'Well, Chris McAlister and Ben Ferrin, what are you doing here? Did you get tired of washing gold and give up on it and leave your claims?'

" 'Well, no, not that,'' said Ben, 'we made a tidy stake and sold our claims to Bob and Ellis Frank. They are still a few miles out. But we got most of their money and we are flush. We put it in the bank and when we heard about you, we came over. How are you doing and how did Etienne come to be here?'

" 'Now, Ben, be calm,' I replied. 'I got to a mudhole and dug down to water and got better and Etienne came by guiding another group and they gave me a horse to ride and we got into the mountains after finding one of Etienne's old waterholes less than four miles from where you left me. How did your party get along? Did you all get through all right?'

" 'Yes, David, we nearly died but finally got to a spring late that day. We all got claims and all have nice stakes. How about you two? Did you do any good for yourselves?'

" 'Yes, we found a nice bar and got about ten thousand dollars apiece before the gravel ran out. So we came on down out of the high hills before we got snowed in. We have been taking goods upriver to George Richfield's trading post. We got in late last night and so we were sleeping in this morning. Well, come on in. It is small but warm and dry.'

"So we ate breakfast together and talked about our various fortunes. Then they said Bob and Ellis wanted to get in some supplies and would we pack them over to the claims? They would show us the way. Two days over and one day back. They had two horses apiece and our four would be able to pack the whole lot. So we loaded up the next morning and started out. We got to the claims in a side valley and spent the night catching up on events. They had a nice camp and seemed to be getting out plenty of gold.

"We took two days coming back because we shot four

deer and took the venison in to sell. We were getting a very nice little nest egg again. When we got back to Docktown there was a big lot of goods, so Ben and Chris offered to help pack it back up. We were able to take it all by using their packhorses and our wagon. The freight on that lot amounted to one thousand dollars, and George Richfield seemed well pleased. The country was filling up, business was increasing, and he wanted us to keep on bringing his goods up. We agreed, as we were getting a nice income from that activity. We went on downriver, having got quite a lot of gold to deliver to the bank. We were careful to see that each lot was credited to the proper person and thought that the future held good prospects.

"Back at Docktown we all made camp together and found another big lot ready to take up. That night Ben talked a minute with Chris and then called me and Etienne over to outline their ideas. They wanted to buy out our freighting outfit and business. They would leave us three horses.

" 'You say you would like to find the others of our two parties, so why not go on down to Sacramento and look around there?' they questioned. Etienne and I talked it over and suggested we make one more trip together and then they might make us an offer. So we had another big lot to take up and had good luck. More people wanted us to carry gold down, as George Richfield told us was the case. There were even some bales of beaver pelts. We agreed that by hiding the gold pokes among the pelts there was a reasonable chance we would get through all right. And then there were four of us, so we could help one another.

"Off we went. We got to Docktown in good time. The details of gold deposit were attended to and then Ben and Chris made their offer. 'We will give you eight thousand dollars for your equipment and good will. You get to keep three horses. If you say yes we can complete the deal tonight or tomorrow.' I nodded to Etienne. He nodded to me and we both said, 'O.K.' We signed the papers the next day, which was

22

April 10, 1851. Both parties were well pleased. But we did not get away at once.

"Mr. Stone was interested and consented to the deal. The cabin was on his claim and so he had to give consent. Then he told Etienne that a friend had come to see him, and now that the two of us were free we might like to talk with him. 'Come on over to my cabin,' said Mr. Stone.

"When we got there, he introduced us to Mr. Oscar Lockwood. This Lockwood seemed an able-bodied man. Indeed, he needed to be, for he had a very isolated mining claim. He had come in for supplies, and would we pack them in for him? He would pack a backpack, and if we would do the same the three horses should be able to finish out the load. A thousand dollars for the trip, five days going and back at our leisure.

"We loaded up that evening and set off from Stone's cabin at dusk of a full moon. That let us get away a few miles before stopping for a rest till morning. We were up and going again early and found Mr. Lockwood an interesting man. He told us he had struck out alone and found good pay dirt in an isolated valley. After getting a few thousand dollars worth of dust, he had decided to come talk with George Stone and try to get a good supply of food while the weather was mild. So Stone suggested us and here we were, which pleased him. He proved to be neither a boozer nor a gambler, but a family man determined to get a good stake and get back home to enjoy it. In truth, that was my story also.

"He guided us in such a way that travelers were not apt to find trace of us and bring unfriendly people to his area. He had sent a thousand dollars home and would send more as he could. We killed a few grouse and did very well for eats. When we reached his rough camp, we found he had got together enough suitable logs to build a ten-by-twelve-foot cabin and was still using an outdoor campfire. "Now you two get settled and unpack and I will attend to a chore that awaits me."

"We did not really pay attention when he left nor note which way he went, but in an hour, as we sat by the fire watching the horses graze, he came back staggering under the weight of a fine deer. He hung his bow on the back of a tree and said, 'I used an arrow so as not to call the attention of any wanderer. Now let us get some fresh meat cooking.'

"After supper Mr. Lockwood asked if for a hundred dollars we would stay over and help him get his cabin up. He had a sharp axe and I had my froe and brace and bit in the saddlebag. So we stayed two days and got the walls and roof in place. He could put in the finishing touches at his leisure.

"Going back, Etienne took the lead and made sure it would take an expert to find our trail. Having been gone a week when we got back to Stone's, we found Orrin and Chris returned also.

"They had another idea and said Mr. Stone had agreed they could fence a corner of his group of claims and so have a corral. Also, they could have part of it for a garden. Would we, for five hundred dollars, make a wooden harrow and a wooden plow? We remembered that part of the big oak trees was left and we decided it could be done and we were just the men who would do it.

"So we got together several pieces four feet long and mortised crosspieces on top of them, pinning them tight with oaken pegs. Then we bored holes at eight-inch intervals for the pegs for the harrow teeth. When we had made thirty holes and filled them with pegs and wedged the tops tight, we set about getting a wooden plow. We found part of the treetop that had a big limb jutting out at an angle. This we shaped so as to serve as a beam, and the limb we shaped for a stirring plow. They could stir the ground and could smooth it with the harrow and then plant the seed.

"I took a close look through my saddlebags and found a packet wrapped in canvas which contained garden seeds. My dear wife had put that parcel in the bag over a year ago. I had brought some winter onion sets and had planted some at the Jackpot. We did not eat all of them and some made top sets, which I had brought with me. All these were turned over to Ben for their garden. Lettuce, radishes, turnips, cabbages, carrots, peas, beans. A few of each, but fine to start with, and they could save seed for a bigger garden next year.

"We planned to be far gone. We started for Sacramento. We noted the newer ways to get gold: sluices, rockers and even pumps to fill the sluices. Ben and Chris had handed us one thousand dollars saying that we should buy them a set of leather harnesses if we could and send it up to them at Docktown. But as we journeyed along there did not seem to be any such item to be had. We did indeed find a ranch where old apple and plum and cherry trees grew. I bought some cider vinegar and some honey, as my supply had been used up. This ranch was proof that good crops would be produced in California. And, indeed, miners bought up all the produce the farmers would sell at big prices.

"At Sacramento we were face-to-face with the giant progress the gold rush had fostered. Big warehouses. Banks. Many saloons, which we avoided like the plague. We still did not see harnesses for sale. At the bank, we deposited the letters of credit from the Docktown bank. As we stepped to the bank door we met George Bunch. We had a good talk with him and his partner, Fred Cook. They had a camp on the edge of town with a friend and insisted we go along and stay with them. There was grass for the horses and room for us. That night we compared stories. They had gotten good claims and washed out several thousand dollars in gold and sold to two other of our bunch, namely Edward King and John Anderson. We told them about cleaning out the Jackpot and freighting to Richfield's store and then selling out to Ben Ferrin and Chris McAlister.

"Jell Taylor, who owned the land they had camped on, came by and told of a man who needed help in building a new warehouse. So next morning four of us went to work for Mike Clayton. That job paid each of us fifteen dollars a day and it took six days. Meantime, I told of my wish to get in touch with all of our bunch still living, and also with Etienne's group. Bunch said I should advertise in the newspaper.

"We decided to visit King and Anderson. All four of us

went there. Three days to get there, followed by a two-day stay. They were getting plenty of gold and planning to get more. We told them of Ben Ferrin and Chris McAlister and Bob McAlister and Ellis Frank. So we had track of nine of our original group, and Etienne Ronald made ten. But of his group, not one had crossed our path. He and I would soon move on to San Francisco, and Bunch and Cook planned to go with us. So my project was moving forward. Going back to Sacramento, we took time to get four deer and we made sale of all the venison we could spare at high prices.

"There was another warehouse being built that needed extra hands. So we four got busy. We might as well draw wages while waiting for answer to the ad. Indeed, as I look back, it seemed that working for wages in those boom times was on average about as profitable as mining. I did think so then and I do now. We were at that ten days and, when we got done, it seemed as though enough time had passed to bring us word of our absent friends. And in fact there was news of them.

"A letter from Joe Black stated he and Bill Wilson and Fritz Gordon were together and would come to see us at Sacramento. He had my own horse and would bring it. And the next day a letter came from Frank Walton saying that that bunch had stayed together and made good stakes and sold their claims. They planned to see us in Sacramento about May 20. That would complete the roster. It seemed providential that every member of both groups—a total of nineteen men—had survived and prospered. It seemed foreordained in a way that the two groups should come together, and most of us, it seemed, planned to go on together.

"In fact, that is what occurred. When the men all got regathered they decided to stick together and go on to San Francisco to get to know more of this big booming land. There were now thirteen men and fifteen horses planning to move together.

"We went cross country toward Oakland, where we arrived late. The men could ride across to Frisco that evening, but a barge to carry the horses would not go till early morning. So we all waited and crossed together.

"By noon we had found a livery stable where the horses could be cared for. The owner said we could make our camp on the twenty-acre tract where he had his stable.

"So we made camp and got organized. George Bunch was chosen captain. We decided two men should at all times be at camp. The rest of us would look over the town and meet at four P.M. at camp. After lunch we started out. Most of us carried cash and also letters of credit. We went to the bank with our letters. Then we scattered.

"I went down to the waterfront. There was an idle ship. A lone man stood on deck. When I approached, he came ashore and told me his name was Norman Burton. He said he owned the *River Queen* but all his crew had gone off to the mines. So he just kept the ship in good order waiting for what the Almighty had in store. When he learned about our group he took a keen interest. Could I bring two more men in a couple of hours. "See, I have a net and know where to find schools of fish. I have two rowboats and with the four of you, you men can well catch some fine fish.' I looked the ship over, asked him if he would lease the ship for four weeks for five hundred dollars. He could stay on as captain and we would see that the regular trip for fish could be taken. I said I would return with the two men; he would wait his answer until that time.

"Just then a man came to see Burton. He introduced me to Henry Gott. This Gott said, 'Mr. Burton, all that lumber I bought from you is just lying there. I cannot get nails. What will I do?'

"I said, 'Mr. Gott, show me your lumber pile. Tell me your plans. There are thirteen of us who have just arrived. Perhaps we can aid you.'

" 'All right, come on.'

"So when I got to the site, I saw he had already got a stone foundation laid—without mortar but straight and solid. Great planks lay there, most of them twenty feet long, and big timbers for joists and sills. The warehouse would be forty by sixty feet and two stories high.

" 'Now, Mr. Gott, my friends will be along in an hour and you must tell us how much you will pay. Many of us understand how to build without nails. We use wooden pegs in holes we bore. I was born in such a house.'

" 'I care not how you build,' he said, 'but if you can put that building up in four weeks, I will pay twelve thousand dollars and many thanks besides.'

" 'We will talk it over, Mr. Gott,' I replied. 'See you in an hour.'

"So back at camp there was plenty to talk about. A man had asked Mr. Rivers, the livery man, whom he could get to make a pack trip. There would need to be at least twelve horses. So Rivers sent him to our camp and he told us what was needed. A wealthy man with many acres of gold-bearing land had a group of Mexicans working. They needed supplies. He would pay fifteen thousand dollars for a trip with our fifteen horses and would need two men. He would go along and help. His name was Jed Young. Bill Wilson and Frank Wilton said they would go. We told him to come back at seven that evening and we would give him our answer. I then told about the ship and suggested George Bunch and Fred Cook go with me and go fishing. I asked Etienne to come along, for I trusted his judgment. So off we went. At Gott's lumber pile, I told about the job offer and the three looked it over and agreed that we might well do that job. They all understood about building with pegs instead of nails. 'All right, Mr. Gott,' we said. 'Eight men will be here tomorrow.'

"We then went on to the ship. Captain Burton was ready. I said, 'Here are George Bunch and Fred Cook to help us fish, and this is Etienne Ronald who will stay here. If you will lease us the ship for four weeks for five hundred dollars we will pay you now. And also, would you sell it to us?'

" 'Well, Mr. LaFollette,' he said, 'if you will leave me be captain, I will train you to sail this ship and we will fish every favorable time as suggested. Tonight what we get will be half for me and half for you. Pay me ten thousand dollars and the ship is yours in four weeks. The five hundred dollars will make part of the price.' So we went aboard leaving Etienne ashore.

"Captain Burton cast off and told me to take hold of various ropes and how to pull and tie. I had climbed ropes at our haymow at home but was not really adept at it. When, with a favorable breeze, we got to the spot chosen he anchored in the shallow water and told me to help lower a rowboat. Bunch and Cook had the other rowboat. They were old hands on the Mississippi and did very well. That made Captain Burton feel fine. We rowed a short distance and he left one end of the net with Bunch. We rowed away and let out the net. Then in a short time we circled and brought the rowboats together and brailed the net over our boat. We had a nice lot of fine flapping fish. Then we spread the net again and brailed it in to Bunch's boat. When we got back to the ship we hoisted the boats aboard. We had near eight hundred pounds of fish. Back at the wharf, Etienne agreed we ought to lease the ship and buy it for ten thousand dollars. We talked with Captain Burton about it and told him at least seven of us would come back to live aboard and that on future fishing trips we thought that half of the fish should accrue to the ship, the other half to be divided equally between Captain Burton and the men. We took our half to the camp and on the way told the fish-mongers to go buy Captain Burton's fish.

"At camp we had a fine fish feed, and when Jed Young came we gave him a share too. We had decided to take up his deal; Bill Wilson and Frank Wilton would go with him. The others would help build the warehouse. Seven of us would go to the ship that night to live. We would always have two at the camp and we would change in turn so that each one might have a day or two loafing at camp. As many as wished would live at the ship, but there must always be two at camp. Jed Young told us that the pack train would load at Oakland and the horses would have to cross on the first barge. So all was arranged.

"George Bunch, Fred Cook, Joe Black, Fritz Gordon, Brad Davis, myself and Pete Wilkins took our bed rolls and walked over to the ship. We found Captain Burton had kept the ship neat and clean. There was a good galley to cook our meals in and plenty of bunks to sleep in. We got acquainted with the good captain and talked over our future plans. But early to bed. That night as I lay in bed, it seemed to me that it would be pleasant to be gently rocked to sleep by the ceaseless waves. I had the idea that this whole adventure was planned by God, because how else but by foreordination could we have gotten such quick jobs for the horses and the men. Jobs we were fitted for and which were ready and waiting for our arrival. On this thought, I fell asleep.

"Next day, Bunch was chosen master builder. We got the great eight-by-twelve timbers laid on the stone foundation. We put three-by-eights flat on the twelve-inch surface and managed to get these to lap over the joints. We mortised the corners of the sills. When we got that done, we started boring holes for the pegs. My brace and bit were in steady use. I checked over the ship's tool chests and found three-and-a-half-inch augers besides two brace-and-bit sets and also several two-inch and one-inch wimbles.

"The twenty-feet sills made three to the length and two across. There was even a middle stone foundation lengthwise. When getting the three-by-eight plank on top of the sills, we found that there were odd chunks of surplus. We used these for pegs. There were several handsaws and adzes and chisels on ship which came in handy. We found that boring the holes was a hard, tedious task. We changed off so that no one bored holes over half a day at a time. When we got the three sixty-foot sills in place, we pegged down the three-by-eight flat on top. The cross sills had to be mortised in snugly.

"Now we had the foundation laid. The job of getting the twelve posts in place and the sills on them for the second story at first seemed impossible. But we took counsel and decided to get one line of posts together with the upper sills, which were eight by ten. We did this on the ground on a plank false work. This was for the first four posts for the middle row. We were able to shape the eight-by-ten timbers to fit and peg the three-by-sixes along the side, which would be the bottom when in place. These were then mortised to the posts so as to form a cap. We braced them well with one-by-eights pegged diagonally. Then with ropes and pulleys, we rigged an assembly to raise the line into place, having first shaped the bottom of the posts to fit the tenons into sockets in the foundation. Then seven men manned the ropes and pulleys and two stood with two-by-four pieces to prop the assembly in place. We succeeded in getting the middle four up with cap on top as pegged. Then we pegged braces to hold it plumb and mortised braces lengthwise so all was firm.

"This procedure was similar to stepping a mast, and Captain Burton viewed our success with shining eyes, for we in effect stepped four masts at once. Then with the middle firm we proceeded to repeat with the sides and at last were able to see the frame of the lower story in place, square and plumb. Then we placed a few one-by-twelve planks across the two spaces and had a workable frame to continue from. Then two across at the bottom of each post, and up went the siding. We bored three holes in each end. That made six holes in each plank eight feet long. Having got one pegged next to the middle post, we then put in some false work using a thin shim to keep that platform just clear of the next plank to be put in place. We were able by using draw knives and planes to fit the siding sugly in place. As each piece went in place, by putting wedges inside the edge of the false work, we wedged it snug against the three-by-six at top and bottom. Then the men got busy boring through the holes into the three-by-six. That way we could fasten the siding tightly in place. We started at the left end post and at the two middle posts at each side so that several men could work the augers at once as soon as the top and bottom holes were pegged. This process was repeated till the whole side was planked. Both outer sides were planked, and then we put in place several two-by-twelve flooring planks so as to give a working surface. We put the complete floor on the top so as to have a working surface to raise the twelve posts and caps into the mortised holes we had made as we had done on the bottom. Repeating the process, we got the twelve upper posts with their capping beams up by means of the ship's rope and pulleys and windlasses. So now we had the two-story frame up and we took good care to brace it well.

"The top floor of two-by-twelve plank went in place, and we now had a working platform to use while installing the roof. We set up the frame for a roof six feet at the peak above the top floor. Some of the one-by-twelve plank were twenty-four feet long, which was lucky in that there were enough to cover a roof requiring one hundred and twenty planks. When we placed them, we spaced them a bit apart and then had to put one-by-four slats over the spaces so as to make a rainproof roof.

"At the north end, we made a frame of heavy timbers projecting three feet at the top so as to be able to rig a pulley to allow Mr. Henry Gott to lift heavy goods to the upper story. We got the roof in place and the two sides enclosed and heaved a sigh of relief. There had been bright weather so far, but now if rain came, who cared? We could work on the bottom floor and the end siding.

"We made doors ten feet wide at each end of each bay. Thus it would be possible to drive a wagon through if that seemed best. Each door was a double leaf, and the doors swung out. We made strong sloping approaches so as to help the loaded wagons get onto and off the floor smoothly. William Branmann came and observed our labors several times and said to George Bunch that he would like to get a group like us to work for him. But we never did. In fact, we later heard that he had not paid his employees promptly, so we were spared that grief. Henry Gott was well pleased and paid us promptly. And why not? We had done the job ahead of time. Etienne was heard to exclaim that we were getting this warehouse built just at the right time. He remembered that as a lad in St. Louis he had often heard carpenters advise putting the lumber together in the month of August. That way there would be no season cracks. And, indeed, the dry climate had tended to season that great stack of lumber. To be sure, there was fog most mornings, which often did not clear away till mid-afternoon. We worked six days a week and we detailed three men to go with Captain Burton and take a haul of fish. As time passed, that haul often amounted to four hundred pounds. Fishmongers came to the ship to buy and paid a dollar a pound at shipside. We ate some and sold the rest so that we had plenty to buy flour and other staples, though prices were very high. At our request, Captain Burton often took us out on a Sunday afternoon to get us trained as sailors. Most of us proved clumsy. Even I, though able to climb a rope, was slow and had to learn the various duties about the sails and masts. Each of us had become able to steer fairly well, and having a few days left of the four weeks, we asked Captain Burton to give us some more lessons in setting sail and reading the sun. He assented and said, 'Gentlemen, you have done well. However, on any voyage there must be a captain and first and second mates. These officers stand watch around the clock. Having observed each of you for several weeks, it seems to me two of you are best fitted for that task. George Bunch would do well as first mate and Fred Cook might pass as second mate. On a voyage, one of the three would be in command and the rest are their crew. If you agree, let us take a short overnight trip and try out our skills.'

"We agreed, and the good captain took pains to teach us how to set and reef and spread the different sails. He had us practice getting aloft and imparted to us most of the main points of the knowledge needed to become able seamen. We needed that.

"In the meantime, back at camp, Boyd Ryan had observed the lay of the ground and thought he would like to take up farming. He talked of leasing a ten-acre tract and raising produce for the market. He saw the manure pile Rivers had about and believed that it would be good to use for a compost pile. When he asked Mr. Rivers if it would be available and also where to find a suitable tract, that gentleman had a suggestion:

" 'Why don't you go see Señor Ramon Blanco? I buy my hay and grain from him. His workmen have scooted off to the mines, so there is no one to harvest the crops. Come, I will take you over to his rancho and make you acquainted.'

"They went and Señor Blanco seemed anxious to get help. Yes, he would pay well. The wheat and barley and oats were ripe for the sickle. Boyd agreed and came back to tell Phil Hume and Dan Hunt. Meantime, our trial voyage ended and we all went over to camp and learned of this farming idea. It was agreed that seven of us would go and work for Señor Blanco. We wanted a man at camp and one at the *River Queen* at all times. So Boyd, Phil, Dan, George, Fred and Joe went to work at the farm along with Brad Davis. They were to receive ten dollars per day.

"Etienne stayed at camp and Fritz Gordon at the ship the first few days. I wanted to look over the town and also make sure all the ropes and tools were stowed away in their proper places on board ship. That done, I went out to see the others at work. They had three cradles to cut wheat and a couple of scythes. With the cradles they could cut the wheat so as to leave it lie in windrows. Other men could gather it into bundles and take two wisks of the straw and twist it in such a way as to hold it in a sheaf. They stood these on end in shocks to finish drying them and to ready them for the flail. When dry enough, the oxen-drawn wagons took it into the great barn to be threshed out with flails. It was hot, but ten dollars a day enticed them to perform that sweaty labor. I even stood up a few shocks myself, being adept at that task from my youth. Then I looked around the farm, or rancho as it was called in California. Finally I was able to see Señor Blanco and found him a very fine Spanish gentleman who could converse in English. This rancho had been in the possession of the Blanco family for a hundred years and had well-arranged dwellings and corrals and barns and fields of wheat, oats, barley and even corn and alfalfa. There was a large garden with potatoes, cabbage, squash, beans, carrots and turnips. I even saw some comfrey and several hives of bees among the orchard trees. I made so bold as to ask if he would sell me some vinegar. Yes, he had barrels of it, and big kegs of honey. He was kind enough to sell me a fifteen-gallon keg of vinegar and a similar-sized keg of honey. Also, he would sell me some comfrey. I seemed to perceive a look of approval in his eyes when I made these purchases. He had no doubt inherited from remote ancestors the knowledge of the usefulness of these items in maintaining health. As, indeed, I had inherited that knowledge. I went on back to the ship with my treasured foods. Then to the camp where the pack train had just returned.

"Jed Young came with them and paid the ten thousand dollars, as promised. He also said he needed to make a return trip in a day or two. This presented a problem. Bill Wilson did not wish to go on a trip again. Etienne Ronald spoke up, 'I would like to take that trip. I keep hoping to get word of John Fremont. He is said to be in this area. He is an old friend, as I once served as a scout for him.'

"So it was agreed. All of us took counsel that evening. We had twenty-five thousand dollars to divide. Twelve of us meant two thousand dollars each, with one thousand dollars extra. They voted to give five hundred dollars extra each to Etienne and myself since each of us had two horses on the trip. Then, what about buying the *River Queen*? We had the money in hand. So eight of us decided to buy the ship. Accordingly, we went over to the *River Queen* and paid Captain Burton. We wished him to stay on as captain and keep up the fishing and training trips. Any profits would be divided in the same way we had divided the fish.

"He agreed to that, for, indeed, he needed a place to live. In such a plan he would make some money and, besides, he would be on his beloved *River Queen* even if others had title. The papers were made out and the money paid over. That was a source of secret satisfaction to me, as will later be plain.

"Next day, Etienne and Frank Wilton set out for the pack trip. One of the others was at camp and one of us at the ship. That left some of us free to look over the town. I was among them. Pete Wilkins and I passed by Gott's warehouse and found him busy checking over the huge building and laying plans to make best use of the storage space. Some ship had come to port, and he had bought part of the cargo. This was being delivered today. At this time, a well-dressed man came up to Mr. Gott and talked with him for a while. Then both men came over to us.

" 'Here, gentlemen,' said Mr. Gott, 'is a friend, Carl Caldwell. He has something to say to you. Mr. Caldwell, this is David LaFollette and Pete Wilkins. Tell them your story.'

" 'That is easy to tell, gentlemen. My problem is this. I have lumber. I have a stone foundation laid, but no nails. This big warehouse is proof that your group can erect a building without nails. Now, will you build mine?'

"We replied, 'Mr. Caldwell, show us the site and plans. Take us over to it now. Perhaps we can get an idea of what is wanted. Then we will consider what can be done.'

"The site was in the direction of River's stable, but a little bit to one side. The lumber seemed sufficient. The building would be only one story high, so we agreed that the group would decide about it that night and meet him at the site the next day with our answer. That night at camp we compared notes and, after laying out the problem, asked for comment.

"Pete spoke up. 'We could take the job on. Six of us would work at the building for Caldwell. When ready, some men now working for Blanco could lay off there and help us get the frame erect. Then we would only need four to complete the building. The others could go on and get Señor Blanco's crops harvested.' We all agreed, and so Pete and I and four others went and told Mr. Caldwell our plan.

" 'I will pay you eight thousand dollars and expect you to get this building done in four weeks,' said Mr. Caldwell.

"Having settled the terms, we got our tools and laid out the working area and got the sills on the foundation. This work went along nicely. We were becoming practiced at this type of construction by this time, and the weather favored us again. The men changed off from work at Señor Blanco's and from guarding camp, and the *River Queen* was in Captain Burton's care. We detailed three to go with him fishing, and if the tide was with us, we often got four hundred pounds six days a week. That kept Burton in funds and the rest of us in food and pocket money. The building was finished well ahead of schedule and paid for. We decided to pool our income from the building and the work at the ranch. The fishing income went as decided before, but only to the eight who had bought the ship.

"I was more and more firm in the conviction that this whole adventure was foreordained. Otherwise, why did it proceed so well? I made another payment to the family in Jasper County. The banks took care to see that it was safely delivered. That was a great relief to me. My thoughts often lingered on my family and I hoped and prayed they would thrive. My belief is that everyone of the eight in the *River Queen* deal was in a situation similar to mine. Else, why did they buy it?

"Captain Burton told us that tides were such that we could hope to get good hauls of fish twice daily if we went out that many times. So why not? We did. Often we would get eight hundred pounds in one day. Some of us went over to help harvest Señor Blanco's crops. The wheat was all in shock. Then it was time to get the barley into the shock, then the oats. By that time, the wheat had dried enough to be taken into the threshing floor. There the flails were put to work and the golden grain pounded out. Then it was wind out and the chaff and straw was taken away. There were storage bins for keeping the grain till it was sold. The oats and barley were threshed in their turn. Then the crew were busy mowing alfalfa. While the alfalfa cured, they dug potatoes. The cured alfalfa was partly put in the great hay lofts in the barn. Part went into stacks out in the open. I took my turn at this kind of work and while at it the word got around that Señor Blanco might lease the whole ranch to Boyd Ryan. Bill Wilson was part of a group of four who favored farming. This group went to the aging Blanco and offered to buy the ranch. They would pay fifty thousand dollars, and since they needed Señor Blanco's advice on carrying on the farm work he could continue living on the farm as long as he lived. Also, he would be allowed to take whatever crops were needed for his own food.

" 'Gentlemen,' he replied, 'that is a very good offer you have made. My children are all gone away to the mines and I am helpless to take care of the work here alone. So if you will pay me forty thousand dollars down and the rest in two years, it will be a great favor to me. Let us go and get the bank to make out the papers.'

"The present crop was to be his after paying the wages agreed on. That was settled, and Boyd Ryan, Phil Hume, Dan Hunt and Bill Wilson became the owners of the Blanco farm. Their wages and gold dust were more than enough to furnish forty thousand dollars; after paying this amount, they still had a tidy sum left for operating expenses.

"While these things were being taken care of, along came Etienne, Frank Wilton and Jed Young. Young was anxious to make another trip as soon as it could be managed. Etienne and Frank were favorably disposed, and when we got the receipts pooled each of us had a fine sum. That settled, there was a surprise.

"Etienne said, 'My friends, on this trip I learned that my friend Fremont owned the land and the gold the Mexican miners were getting out. I would like to buy the whole pack train. I would pay ten thousand dollars for those horses. What do you say?' After consulting among ourselves, we answered that he and Frank had best make another trip. When they returned we might well be sufficiently settled in our own designs to seriously consider his offer.

"That night at the ship we told Captain Burton of these happenings. He looked thoughtful a few minutes, then made a surprising statement:

" 'Gentlemen, I am certain that every one of this group who have bought this ship are hoping to be able to sail it to Panama this winter. Because each one has a family at home and you wish to join them. How about it? Am I right?'

"George Bunch replied, 'Indeed, Captain, that is just my idea. But about the others—they have never said anything like that.'

"Then each in turn answered that such were his hopes. 'But,' I said, 'how did you get such an idea, Captain Burton?'

" 'That is the only thing that could explain your acts and your anxious tries to learn to handle the ship. And you have done well. Perhaps your hopes can come to pass. But do you wish me to continue training you and to act as your captain even as far as Panama, where I have never been?'

"We looked at one another. We had in truth never considered any other situation, but no one had talked about it. Yes, we wanted Captain Burton to be our captain. We told him so.

" 'Well, in that case I am willing to undertake it. However, you are far from being a ship's crew able to sail the open ocean. Sure, you have each learned to steer by the compass after a fashion. You have each learned to take sight from the sun and the stars after a fashion. This latter is a part that only the officers really need to know, and Bunch and Cook do quite well at it. I saw at first they had been aboard ships before. My idea is that we make a trip over to Oakland and practice handling the ship. Then next week we might plan to take a load of freight to Sacramento if it can be gotten. In that case we need a supercargo to keep the accounts and to take charge of the freight. I believe that David is the best man for that. Do you agree?' They answered yes, and I became supercargo.

"The next day was Sunday, so there was no work at the ranch. After church, the eight owners took four guests on a short sail to Oakland. Captain Burton had us practice setting the sails and trimming them and furling them. I confess I was still clumsy, though climbing ropes was a childhood habit. The others had most of them been in sail- or rowboats along the Ohio or Mississippi rivers and were a little more proficient.

But we got to Oakland and anchored, set sail again and made our way back to the old anchorage and tied up in good time.

"The next day, Monday, most of the men went to help harvest at the Blanco ranch. After Captain Burton agreed it might be a good idea to buy wheat from Señor Blanco, thither I went also and found that good man would sell seventy-five bushels at two dollars a bushel. He would deliver the wheat the next day at the *River Queen*, but we must have bags to put it in. We would pay at shipside.

"That sent me to looking for sacks. First I went to the bakery to get empty flour sacks. But the baker suggested I go to the mill. When I got there it was evident they had plenty of empty sacks. So I bought forty sacks that should hold two bushel each. That cost eight dollars. When Captain Burton heard what I had done he said it was fine.

"There was a ship moored alongside the *River Queen* which had come in only that day. Captain Burton said its captain was a friend of his and introduced me to Captain Hook, who owned the ship. It was fresh downcoast from Portland, Oregon, and had a cargo consisting mostly of freshly harvested wheat. I asked Captain Burton how much freight he wished to take on. He thought he could comfortably haul four hundred tons. The Blanco wheat would at most weigh two and a quarter tons. Why should we neglect a chance to buy the wheat Hook had just brought? We decided to take a look at it, and approached Captain Hook. I wanted Captain Burton with me on that big a deal, so he went along and pronounced the wheat excellent. 'How much do you want per bushel?' I asked.

" 'I want a dollar seventy-five a bushel, and more if you do not take it all,' replied the captain. I looked at Captain Burton. He nodded, so I said we would take all three hundred and fifty tons. We started transferring the wheat to the *River Queen* at once. Captain Burton took charge of seeing that it was stowed properly. We were still at it next day when Señor Blanco's wagons came. We had to put that wheat into sacks and while at that a thought occurred to me. Why not buy cabbage, potatoes and carrots, a ton of each? Captain Burton agreed. I bought sixty more sacks and went back with the wagons to see if Señor Blanco could spare that much. 'Bueno,' he said. The price would be forty dollars per ton and we could expect delivery that evening. I suggested that they put the produce in sacks at the ranch. So we were getting a cargo. Captain Burton seemed pleased and we were busy getting all stowed when I spied something on the deck of the *Speedwell*, as Captain Hook's ship was named. I quickly went over there and asked Captain Hook if the wagon I had noticed was for sale. It was new and he said he would sell it for four hundred dollars. What about the harness? Yes, he had four sets of harnesses, enough for a four-horse team with collar size 17½ and lines of leather. He would sell the harnesses complete for three hundred dollars. I thought about the thousand dollars Ben Ferrin had put in my hands. I paid for the wagon and harnesses and had them put aboard the *River Queen*. I asked Captain Burton what the freight ought to be for taking them along. He set the price at fifty dollars, so that was that.

"The next day was Wednesday, and all eight of us were aboard as the ship cast off on the way to Sacramento. The wind was coming straight in our face after we got away from the moorage. Bunch, as first mate, was in charge at first. I was puzzled about how we would ever get to Sacramento against that wind and asked Frank Cook about it.

" 'Oh, that is possible. We tack. Note that the boat is moving a little starboard and not exactly straight to Sacramento. When we get too far that way, we luff. That is, the steersman turns the helm so that we come about into the face of the breeze and on over past to the port side. With the sails set properly we can sail forward but not directly forward. When we get over too far to port we steer the ship back over to the starboard. When the yardarm swings over as the ship turns we must take care, because it can break a leg if we get in its way. Otherwise, it is an easy trick to get to Sacramento by zig-zag. Of course, we could go faster if we had a tailwind but the tide is in our favor and we can make fair headway.'

"We did not get to Sacramento that day. For one thing, we drew close to a point where there was shallow water, and, probably would be fish. Or Captain Burton thought so, and directed the ship in that direction. Sure enough, the gulls were dipping after herring which came to the surface to get away from the large fish gulping at them from below. We anchored and got out the rowboats and nets. The haul was about four hundred pounds. Then we repeated after dumping the fish in tanks Captain Burton had provided. In all we got near four thousand pounds of fish.

"The next day we reached Sacramento. There we found ready sale for fish and wheat and potatoes and cabbage. But talk was that at Docktown anything brought higher prices. In fact, here came a man who offered four dollars and fifty cents a bushel for wheat and six cents a pound for spuds, and more for cabbage and carrots. There was a condition—these were delivery prices at Docktown. Captain thought it over and looked at the river and the water depth. Finally, he made up his mind. We would sell half our cargo here, and with the lightened ship, he thought we might get to Docktown. His ship had been built to sail shallow streams and should get up there handily. We could at least try it. So while daylight lasted we set out. The breeze was at our backs and the current was sluggish. We anchored at dusk.

"It was three days getting to Docktown. We even put out the rowboats to help the ship upstream in spots. At Docktown we met Mr. Stone and sold our cargo to the man who offered those high prices. Fish here brought three dollars a pound. We had brought a ton. We received six thousand dollars for them, a tidy sum for the vegetables and four-fifty a bushel for wheat that cost a dollar eighty at average. We laid overnight there, and met the next day with Ben Ferrin and Chris McAlister. When I showed them their wagon, which we had unloaded and set up with the harnesses, they were delighted. They were happy, too, when they received the balance of $250 coming to them.

"We made it back to Sacramento in a day and a half and

even had some freight to carry on the way. It was fortunate that the water remained fairly deep. We took stock of our venture. We had nearly trebled our costs, which were near $18,500. Our return was $51,000. That was a nice voyage. We had a hundred tons of freight to take back to Frisco at twenty dollars, which added two thousand dollars to our take, and we hauled in 4,000 pounds of fish, which we got at the shallow. That added four thousand dollars to make a total of $57,000 taken on that voyage. One-half went to the ship, which was $28,500, one-fourth to the crew was $14,250, one-fourth to Captain Burton was another $14,250. Few mines could match this income. The $14,250 divided between eight men made a total of $5,347.50 each for, at most, two weeks' work. Etienne and I had done well at the Jackpot, but not this well.

"When we got rid of the fish and the freight at Frisco, we cast up our accounts. The figuring really was up to me as supercargo. Each one of us was pleased, and so was Captain Burton. That evening he told us that we were getting to be better sailors as the days passed, but that we had never been out of sight of land. That would be much different. What he had in mind was, we might take a trip outside the Golden Gate and try our hand at taking fish if we could find a good spot. We would need to clean and tidy ship tomorrow and take on supplies for a week. We need not use over three days on this first voyage, but if a storm came up we might be out for a week. So better be prepared.

"Next day, we were banking our gains. Then I went out to Blanco and bought a hundred pounds each of onions, carrots, potatoes and cabbage. Also he sold me a hundred pounds of dry beans left over from previous years. He sent in a wagon with the lot and I came back and bought more sacks at the mill. Then to the store where ships outfitted. Hams, bacon, butter, spices, soda, yeast cakes, flour, etc. The prices were high, but our pockets were full. While there, Mr. Gott came in and I told him about our project. We planned to go two days out to sea and then back if we succeeded. A minute later a fine husky sailor came to me and he told about hearing some conversation between us. His name was Nels Wigand.

" 'I am a sailor just in from three years in and around Canton, the Philippines and Hawaii,' he said. 'You said you planned to get fish out in the open sea. If you let me come along, I think I can be of aid to you, for I have fished in many waters. If you like, I would like to show you what you will need and all you will need. What say?'

"I answered, 'Now you interest me. We have done well in the bay with nets. Now you say we will need no nets. What will we need?'

" 'From what I observed outside the Golden Gate,' he replied, 'you will need a stiff heavy rod for each man. A stout line, perhaps eighty feet long and a strong hook. You will need some strips of colored cloth and some string. You will tie a bit of cloth—yellow is best—to each hook. First file off the barb. Such an outfit is all for each man. As I have seen it done, when we reach the school, if we spot one, you will find that fish bite the cloth and you pull in the line with the fish on the hook. On deck the fish snaps off the hook and you then toss it back into the midst of the swimming hordes of fish. You have never witnessed the like. But I have and you will not regret taking me along and doing as I have advised. I saw such schools as our ship came in.'

"The man seemed to know what he was about and, on consideration, I bought such outfits as he advised. Then we went out to the *River Queen* and introduced him to Captain Burton. They talked awhile, and it turned out he knew some of Captain Burton's friends who owned ships in the overseas trade. I told about what Wigand had advised.

" 'Well, now that is news. We can try it. Come aboard and get settled,' the Captain said. Wigand went off to get his duffle and settle in.

"Next morning, an hour after sunup, we set out with an outgoing tide. The day was fine. The view outside the Golden Gate was such as I had never looked at. The long rollers broke upon the beach in foam and rushed back only to repeat. But we looked out to sea and were anxious to get out of sight of land. That came about in time, and before dark we had only the stars and moon to be our guides. Next morning we were still gazing about when Nels spoke to me:

" 'There they are. Get your lines rigged and when we get in their midst, the ship should be kept on the same course the fish are taking.'

"We took his advice. Eight of us stood on deck behind the bulwark and, when among the swimming fish, threw the baited hooks among them. At once each hook was grabbed. At once each man pulled the hooked fish aboard. The fish flapped off. The hook was tossed back into the thronging fish. We could take about three fish a minute. The deck was soon a mass of flopping fish. Tuna was what Nels called them. He and Captain Burton were busy shoving them into the tanks fitted into the hold. This kept up for about four hours. Then the ship was out of the school and our weary arms got a rest. Three fish a minute, a hundred and eighty an hour, seven hundred and twenty apiece time eight equaled 5,760 fish. Three pounds apiece equaled 17,280 pounds. We found another school and repeated the haul before losing pace. Thirty-four thousand pounds of fine fish. Captain Burton thought a moment, and decided to get back to Frisco. We got back in the night. We were praising Nels Wigand and thanking him. We told him of our way of dividing the profits and offered to put him in for an equal part of the crew's share. At daylight, the fishmongers came offering a dollar fifty a pound. That would make $51,000. Again, one-fourth to Captain Burton was $12,750, one-fourth to the nine of us meant $1,417 each, and of course one-half to the eight owners meant $3,500 each. We sold the fish and decided to put in the day about town.

"Before daylight, we cast off for another try at tuna. The moon gave us some light; we were trying to learn to navigate day and night. When well out to sea, we spied another school of tuna and got among them. The action was swift, as on the first voyage, but we could not keep in line over three hours.

However, we found another school soon and did a three-hour stint there. Later we struck another school and got action for two hours. That made eight hours. We started back and made it back that night. We had brought in over 34,000 pounds of fish. Again a $51,000 take. Thus in one week we had for Captain Burton $25,000, each of the nine fishing had $2,834 and the ship's share brought $7,000 to each owner.

"It was now late September and Captain Burton mulled the future. He finally suggested we make a voyage to Portland. He thought we could reach dockside there in less than three weeks. We picked up some freight, but not much. He said we ought to take plenty of supplies and should catch enough tuna to eat and about a ton for sale. In Portland they might like a change from salmon, of which there were great numbers coming up the rivers this time of year. So after taking a day to prepare, off we went.

"This was different. We kept off quite a distance in case a storm from the west might come along. But the weather continued fine, and in just over two weeks we came off the bar at the Columbia River mouth. We stood by so as to catch a favorable tide and got in by daylight. Then it was easy to get up to the Willamette and on up to Portland.

"There we put off what little freight we brought and managed to sell the tuna for a dollar a pound. That was because it was new to them. Then Captain Burton wanted to visit old friends and asked me to see if I could locate a cargo of wheat. I was able to buy all the wheat we wished to carry at eighty cents per bushel. That was because most ships sailing to San Francisco lost their crews there and could not get back to load more wheat.

"So we loaded three hundred and ninety tons of wheat. The cost to us was just over ten thousand dollars. Captain Burton insisted we get a full set of canvas for new sails and new rigging, and some spare spars and a mast. That made the four hundred ton full load, as estimated. We did indeed get some dry goods—good work clothes and new shoes—for there would be few opportunities to outfit ourselves at such prices after we left Portland.

"There had been a gale while we laid up at Portland, but we were snug at the wharf and sustained no damage. Now we took off and managed to cross the dangerous bar into the broad ocean in fine shape. Then Captain Burton insisted we stand far away from shore in case another gale should come along. He told us that he didn't think there would be another storm before we got back to Frisco, but he remembered hearing that usually storms come at forty-day intervals and we would be getting back to Frisco in just about two weeks.

"That was the way it was. We managed to catch a nice ten-ton haul of tuna a day out of Frisco. When we got to Frisco, Captain Burton thought it best to keep on to Sacramento to sell our cargo. There we unloaded the whole cargo, getting four dollars a bushel for the wheat, and the tuna bringing in an additional four thousand, for a grand total of $53,000. That meant that Captain Burton earned about $26,000 for six weeks' work. The nine crewmen earned about $3,000 each, and the eight owners about $13,000, for the ship's share had to pay for the new canvas and rigging. This was a real money harvest for us, and I rejoiced in the blessings God had bestowed on us. The others did so too, I am sure. The captain said we should lay over at Sacramento till the next storm, which came almost exactly after the passage of forty days from the Portland storm. We then cast off for Frisco, but made a four-thousand-pound haul at the shallows on the way. These fish brought six thousand dollars at shipside in Frisco.

"Captain Burton insisted we make an entire new set of sails and said he thought we might well go to Panama after the next storm. Nels Wigand had by this time become a favorite with us all, and even the captain said he could well act as first mate if needed. Nels seemed pleased and agreed to bear a hand on the voyage.

"Captain Burton said, 'Gentlemen, I have kept my word with you, and you have lived up to your bargain. You should be able to take the *River Queen* to Panama. When we get there I would like to buy her back from you if you will sell, or we can continue as we are and I will promise to handle her and take my one-fourth of gain. Please yourselves. You may have plenty of time to talk it over while on the way.'

"I kept thinking about predestination and was more convinced than ever of its reality. If God can control the weather so that sailors can predict storms as Captain Burton did, and God controls the sun and moon and sends the high and low tides in a regular pattern, then He can also direct our lives into channels to please Himself. Certainly, the heavenly bodies obey His will, as every sailor and astronomer realizes.

"While we were getting the new sails in order under Captain Burton's and Nels Wigand's direction, along came Jed Young, Etienne and Frank Wilson. After a huddle to make up our minds, we decided to sell the pack train. Etienne was pleased. Frank had found a ranch he liked and could buy and wanted to drop out of the pack train when it got there, so Etienne found an old friend in Frisco who decided to take Frank Wilson's place. That was settled. The four participants in the Blanco deal were pleased with it, and when the next storm had passed, the old *River Queen* set out to sea with a happy crew intent on getting to Panama.

"Captain Burton again got far out to sea and we saw no land for three weeks. Then, when his study of the skies indicated it was the proper time, he veered to port and took in sails so as to move slowly. At last we spied land. He thought it was an island offshore from Panama, and it proved to be so. We had found a school of tuna and laid in about three tons. Soon after his study of charts showed him where to steer to get to Panama. We felt like jumping into the water and swimming ashore, and one of us actually did. When we anchored, Captain Burton advised the rest of us to stay aboard till he and Nels could row ashore and get to understand the situation. When they got to shore, there was Brad Davis. They asked him to stay by the boat till they came back. After three hours they returned and came aboard. The shore was lined with all kinds of camps and hovels made by stranded gold seekers unable to get passage to Frisco. The fish went fast at a dollar a pound, and when the dealers got on their way in their skiffs, we were left quite a distance away from shore. That is what we wanted. That night we took counsel. Captain Burton offered to buy the ship if we would sell. Nels Wigand wished to stay with the good captain and the good ship *River Queen*. They wished us to stay aboard till they could find suitable men to sail the ship back to Frisco. They suggested that George Bunch and Brad Davis go ashore with Nels and scout around for sailors and they would try to find a way to get across the Isthmus of Panama. Captain Burton thought he could carry three hundred men north in reasonable comfort if they had bedding. He would charge a hundred dollars each. He would also need four good experienced sailors besides Nels. He would charge Nels with finding them. He thought that four others who seemed capable and wished to work their way north would be enough to man the ship.

"Before noon Nels came back with two sailors for Burton to talk with. He agreed they might be first or second mates if needed. They liked the ship. They went ashore with Nels, and together they chose five more that seemed suitable. After Burton talked with them, he was pleased with their bearing. These strangers all went ashore for the night, and Bunch and Davis came back with their information. There was a pack train due to go across in a few days. The owner had lost most of his men to the gold fever and wanted help. If we would go and help keep guard and help with the train, he would pay us fifty dollars each and furnish food. Bunch thought there was a shipment of gold in the packs, as was so often the case during the history of this isthmus since Pizarro's time. We considered the plan and decided to take the offer.

"Captain Burton offered to pay us fifty thousand dollars for the *River Queen*. He would give us twenty-five thousand dollars cash and a draft for twenty-five thousand dollars. We decided to accept the offer. The men said the draft should be made out to me and we would stay together till we reached St. Louis. Then I was to divide the money. This was done and we signed the *River Queen* over to Captain Burton.

"Nels Wigand spoke: 'Gentlemen, I have been pleased to be with you. This is the first group of men who so worked together. Not one of you drink nor gamble nor indulge vile habits. My advice is to stay together. Select a captain. I suggest George Bunch. Always have a guard—two would be better. You could divide the night into two watches, as on shipboard. Every other night another four would be on duty. That way you could all get plenty of rest. You have been fortunate to get this employment. If you get to Colón in good time, you might well find deserted ships there waiting to see men come along who can sail them. You could well make up a crew for such a ship. If so, you would be paid at least as far as New Orleans. From there it ought to be easy to get on up to St. Louis. Tomorrow Captain Burton will try out the new crew. We will sail around the area to learn how they perform their work. I believe they will each one do well. Then we will get ready for the voyage to San Francisco. When we are ready we will take on the passengers and you can camp ashore till the pack train moves out.' That was quite a long speech but it seemed good advice.

"Next day the new crew came aboard. We watched while they worked the ship. They tacked, they reeved in sail, they let it out, they anchored. Captain Burton even went over to a rocky point and took heavy rocks aboard to stow below as ballast. The following day our group took our duffle ashore and observed as the passengers moved aboard. Many planned to sleep on deck. They all got aboard, and the good ship *River Queen* weighed anchor and passed from our view.

"In two days our pack train moved out. There was much discomfort but we were well inured to hard conditions. The owner of the pack train was well pleased when he saw how we worked together, and the fact that we kept regular watch seemed to lift a weight from his shoulders. The pack trail we traveled had been in use since Balboa's time, but was still primitive. A few years later, a railroad was built, but we did not see any evidence of its coming in our tedious journey. It was in the future. The drawing power of gold would in time force the building of a railroad. The trail was a mean one to traverse. Colón was a camp, but little better than the beach at

Panama. We got our pack train to its destination. We got our pay and found a place to camp. We kept up our organization, keeping watch day and night.

"The second day, George Bunch and Fred Cook started out to learn what the prospects were for a passage to New Orleans. They returned late in the afternoon.

"Bunch said, 'The best we can do is a steamship owned by a Kenneth Williams. The ship has a mast and sails also. He has an engineer still with him but lacks a full crew. He wants six men but will take on all eight of us to get to New Orleans. We do not know engines, but the engineer thinks he can teach us what is needed. Captain Williams is glad we understand sails and rigging, for he plans to sail when the wind favors this. If the engine fails, we can still move. That will give the engineer time for repairs, and that is important. Williams will pay us two hundred dollars each if we will stay with the job till we reach New Orleans. I say we should accept the offer.'

"I rubbed my face. We were sitting around a smudge in the hopes that the smoke would keep some of the gnats away. Wigand had given us a salve which he said was much used in Canton to ward off insects. It helped, but not well enough. We were all nearly raw from the bites. We all agreed that the thing to do was to get on that ship. Perhaps the pests would not be so thick there. So we went and made our bargain. There was some relief from insects when we got underway, cleared well away from land, which was very pleasant.

"Captain Williams was a pleasant, courteous man and was obviously very glad to have us with him. His ship, the *Ruby Queen,* was medium-sized and bigger than the *River Queen*. The steam engine was below deck and burned coal. This coal had been barged down the Mississippi to New Orleans, where he had it put aboard for the voyage. If coal ran out then sail was the only means of moving. On a quiet day, sail's were reefed in, but if a stiff, favorable breeze came along then the sails help were of much aid to progress.

"The Gulf of Mexico was the scene of violent storms at times, but we were fortunate in that none approached us. We were quite interested in seeing the flying fish about which we had heard. Some even landed on deck. They did not indeed fly, but gained speed in the water and spurted up and sailed through the air some little distance. We had a few lines and hooks and, when at leisure, some of us tried fishing. It was not like catching tuna, but we got a few which proved a welcome addition to our regular fare. We were all anxious to get to New Orleans and were surprised when we got in sight of land to learn that there were over a hundred miles to pass up the mighty river to the city. The land we saw was one of the islands in the channel; here was where an engine was very useful because, with sails only, it was often necessary to wait for favorable winds.

"It was February 1st when at last we moored and ended that tedious voyage. Our anxious group did not tarry, but wanted to lay aboard till we could gain passage upriver. Here, again, it was the same story. Seamen were anxious to sign on at the *Ruby Queen* to get to Panama. That left the steamers headed upriver shorthanded. Captain readily gave us a good word and, as we were now experienced steamboat men, we soon got aboard a ship and sped upriver. Captain Burke of the paddle-wheeled riverboat *Swift,* was well pleased to get eight able seamen of steady habits. Our pay was a hundred dollars each to St. Louis. There he would have no trouble getting a crew downriver, because so many people wanted to get to Panama and so be on the way to Frisco.

"But our wishes were to return to our families. We got rooms and proceeded to a bank and presented our draft. Then we divided the $25,000, which meant $3,125 each, and with that I have no doubt each of us had over $50,000 at his disposal.

"So we separated. I was able to get passage to Keokuck and there bought a horse and took my duffle along to Ottumwa, to Blakesburg and on north to Jasper County.

"Before reaching there, I stopped overnight at a tavern. To my surprise, there was my brother John. He had come down there with his stallion, Nig, to stand a few days. We rejoiced to see each other. That regular circuit with Nig had gained him quite a sum of cash according to the standards of wealth in that farming country. I was pleased to learn that the family had thrived. They had received the several sums of money sent home at intervals and had plenty of all things.

"The next day we went on home to a very joyful reunion. The children where shy at first, not having seen me for so long, but were growing fast and in blooming health. My wife was pleased to learn of my good fortune and more pleased to know I planned to sell out here and take them all to New Albany. That Indiana town meant friends and kinfolk to her, and so we decided to move fast. A buyer was needed first, and that proved possible. We got ten thousand dollars for the farm and stock. We reserved a good team and my pony and a covered wagon, the same in which we had come five years ago. Half the price was due in cash, the rest at six percent till paid. We told old friends part of our story and received congratulations on getting safely back with a little cash. I think each was very fortunate in that way.

"We began our journey about ten days later. Along the way, John rode Nig and he and I talked over my adventures. I told him my plans were to get brother Jeremiah to join me in a return to California. We planned two ox-drawn covered wagons with plenty of supplies and tools, the better to get out the gold. John was not excited about washing gold. I found out at Blakesburg that he had an interest there at the Easley home. I did not blame him, for he married Angeline Easley almost at once and remained there to become a wealthy farmer and breeder of registered livestock, as our father was in Indiana. I handed him a thousand dollars and knew he had more than that from Nig's fees. John had ready cash and the prospect of regular income from Nig. Indeed, there were six colts fathered by Nig at Blakesburg then. Dr. Gutch came to the wedding limping from a broken leg. It seemed that Dove had run away and wrecked the buggy and broke the good doctor's leg. He was getting old and a bit crotchety. When someone asked Dr. Gutch why Dove had run, he replied, 'There was not anything the matter with her. She is just like my old woman, getting fooler and fooler every day.' But he was getting old.

"For my part, I thought we close-order Baptists, or Hardshells as some people called us, were famous for keeping together and helping each other and working hard and we saved our money, not spending it on trifles. I say we were fortunate and expected to be fortunate and trusted God to guide us to that end. Good health was our lot. We, in fact, invited it, being total abstainers and inheriting good health and the knowledge needed to maintain that health. And we believed in work.

"The wedding over, we said our farewells and proceeded on our way across Illinois and to the loved old log house where I was born. There we told our story to the kinfolk and told our friends of my intention to go west again. Jeremiah fell in with my plans, and we soon got our two covered wagons fitted up and loaded. By May 1st we were on the way. There were others bound in the same direction and there was no trouble about joining up with a dozen other wagons bound for the goldfields. The grass was green and we carried bushels of corn. Though the way was littered with broken wagons and discarded goods left by the past two summers' travelers, we had gotten good wagons and understood how to keep them up. Having plenty of cash, I believed in buying the best. As fate would have it, the other dozen men were like-minded. Not a gambler or a boozer among them. It seems like such men tend to get together. At least our fate seemed to indicate that. After weeks on the road, we came to the campsite near by the big trading post where I had been before. There, to our surprise, we found Etienne Ronald. He told us he had joined Fremont, who had bought his pack string, and in the end came back over the mountains.

" 'I had an idea, David,' he said, 'that you would be coming west again and have been hoping to see you here. Also, Ben Ferrin sold out and came back here too. Let's go find him. I think he will join us, for I intend going back to California again.'

"That is how it turned out. That made four of us with two ox-drawn wagons. Fate again. Then there was the group we came with. That dozen wagons were joined with us, and we all agreed to pay Etienne to guide us. He thought he could direct our way so as to get our wagons safely over the plains and mountains. An agreement was made to pay him a thousand dollars by the time the oxen were well-rested and we were ready to move on.

"We made good time by following almost the same trail as two years before. We were the first along this way that spring of 1852, and the grass was good and the traveling pleasant. At the edge of the mountains, Etienne was able to lead us up ridges and valleys without a great deal of trouble. Slowly we gained to the top. Just over the crest, Jeremiah and I declared we wished to stop and rest the oxen. Etienne went on a few days with Ben. We again took up our journey, and Etienne and Ben came back to meet us, having seen the others to a place from which they could go on alone.

"In camp that night I asked Etienne if he thought he could lead us to that same Jackpot again. I said to Etienne, 'Do you think any gold is left at that bar? At least there should be our snug cabin. Do you and Ben feel like joining up with us to travel and wash gold together?'

" 'Now look here, David,' said Etienne, 'that has been my idea all along, and Ben is of the same mind. That is why we came back to meet you.'

" 'Now that is a comforting feeling. If you two like, we would be honored to have you for partners. So let us make plans to get down to that cabin.'

"Next day, Etienne and Ben started ahead and we started our ox team down along a certain ridge he had pointed out. Later, Ben came back to show us a way they had decided on. We made rather slow progress on account of bushes and trees. Some of them must be cut out of the way, but we tried leaving few signs of our passage and in time, by driving over rocks and down water courses, we had disguised our trail rather well. We made a short stop for lunch, and when we came to a

55

favorable place to camp late in the day, we made a campfire and unyoked the oxen.

"Etienne came in sight in a short time. 'Yes,' he said, 'I found the cabin and there is a surprise for you. That bar has filled up again. It might take two more days to get there from here, and we will take care to leave little trace of the wagons.'

"Jeremiah was curious about our sly plans and asked for the reason behind them. 'Well, brother,' I said. 'If that bar is full of gold as it was before, there is a fortune for us there. And if no one else knows about it, there can be no trouble. There has been much trouble among the gold miners farther down. Robbers, claim jumpers and even murder in camp and along the trails. By keeping our find here secret there is a better opportunity to work out the values in peace and quiet. Why invite trouble?'

"There was plenty of game, grouse, and deer to be easily taken, and the fresh meat was a welcome change from the cured meat on hand. We had even killed several buffalo on the plains and hung the strips of meat to the wagons to dry as we had moved along those hot plains. If cured well, it would keep a long time. Meantime, we could use fresh meat when it was easy to get. We did not need to discuss those things, we had been together so long that these matters were done instinctively.

"When, at last, we arrived at the little clearing, the snug cabin was a pleasant sight. We soon got the oxen turned to grass and hurried with gold pans to the bar. Was there gold there as before? Well, a few pans of gravel revealed that that same kind of coarse gold was there. Then we got our campfire going with ease and cooked a feast. We checked over the cabin. We built a fire in the fireplace, though we had cooked supper at the outside campfire rocks. There were a few winter onions among the weeds, and we made plans to get a garden spot plowed since I had brought a plow and a fine collection of garden seeds and some comfrey roots. Then we slept the sleep of the just. We were just plain tired.

"Next morning, we took our gold pans and made a careful check of the bar and found that gold was there, as in 1850. It was in all parts. We had all seen how gold was recovered in other areas in the previous year and decided to make a sluice. We had the saws and adzes we needed, and a froe, and soon had a workable sluice with cleats across the bottom.

"In a few days we got going in regular fashion. I had brought mercury and a retort. We did not put mercury in the riffle at the top of the sluice. We thought that the coarser particles would lodge there but the finer dust would pass on, so we put mercury there to form an amalgam. We tested to learn the best slope for the sluice. Soon we were working a ten-hour day, and were we getting gold! By using the amalgam, we found that when we refined the gold from it in the retort we were saving more of the precious metal than we had saved by panning in 1850. The four of us were handling lots of gravel.

"By August 15 we had gotten most of the bar worked over. We thought we had about $50,000 worth, counting the raw gold from the upper riffles and the refined gold. In fact, I had brought a scales set to weigh it and thus get an idea of the worth of the product. Then we took thought.

" 'Let's send Jeremiah and Ben down stream to see if another bar is down there,' I suggested. My suggestion resulted in their going down along the channel. By noon they were back.

" 'Yes,' said Ben, 'there is another smaller bar down there and there is a nice lot of gold, but I think it is finer. By using the sluice and mercury we should be making a good haul.'

"The four of us managed to get the sluice floated down the shallow stream, which is all it was now in midsummer. Indeed, the water was the lowest I had ever seen it. While the others worked out the small bar, Etienne and I went after game. There were soon two deer at camp, and we made most of the venison into jerky in the hot sun. By that time, we had lettuce and carrots growing well. Potatoes were up, beans blooming, cabbage heading; we even had cucumbers and beets. It began to look like home, and we thought all the vegetables tasted excellent. We got the deerskins soaking to slip the hair and made ready to tan them.

"We took our pans and checked the nooks and spots along the channel. We were surprised at the gold we got. Mostly coarse. Then we went down to help the others. We had a regular system. One man would come back to camp at about noon and get a kettle of stew and some biscuits to take downtrail to the bar. That way little time was lost traveling. We changed off on that chore, so each man had a respite from handling gravel. By the end of August, the small bar was cleaned up. We thought we had about $20,000 more."

"Mr. Jones," said Ephraim, "this story is a long one. I found it interesting, but we better wait till another day, say two weeks from now, to get the rest of it told. That is, if it still interests you."

"Now see here, my friend," I rejoined, "I am not tired of it. This is one story that holds my interest all the way. By all means, if you will be so kind, let us hear you tell the rest of that oldtime miner's story."

"All right then," replied Ephraim. "In two weeks meet me here and we will go into it again. My old friend told me of his early efforts and because I knew him well, it was of great interest to me."

Dear Reader: As you know, if you have read all of the preceding, this story is by a relative of mine and had a more peculiar interest to me than to Ephraim. Of course, I wanted to hear the rest of it. Two Saturday afternoons later, I met him, eager to hear him continue with my great uncle's words.

Mr. Ephraim told me about a trip he had made for a group of friends. This was in the days after gold had been made worth $35 an ounce. Mine-minded people were checking known large deposits of low-grade gold ore, and he had been helping at an old mining area. He said the values were there. The deposit could be worked at a profit, but one thing was holding it back: What to do with the tailings? It was next to a railroad and there was no room for a tailing pile.

"Well, Mr. Ephraim," I replied, "why not build a bin next to the track and sell the tailings to the railroad for ballast. That ought to please them." I never found out if that ever came to pass.

At the time I am writing this, gold is valued at $120 an ounce. If that gold area is still unworked, there might well be a fine fortune waiting for someone.

But to get back to the twice-told story of David LaFollette, Ephraim took up the tale again two weeks later.

"We held counsel again. What were we to do? Finally, in view of the fact we had worked out the two bars, who could tell what was best to attempt? Finally Etienne said, 'Gentlemen, I have been thinking about the fact that the Jackpot bar held coarser gold than the Tinpot bar and the gold deposits many miles downstream are finer yet. What can we think but that there might be coarser gold to be found farther upstream from here. Suppose we detail Jeremiah and Ben to take a walk upstream and see if another bar can be found. Meanwhile, David and I will tan the skins and search the pockets near the Jackpot. What do you think?'

"That was food for thought. They were younger and spryer than we, and they were willing, as we could see from their sparkling eyes. It seemed a good idea.

"The next morning they took food for a few days in their pack sacks and started upriver. Meanwhile, we at camp tried turning over rock in the channel edge.

"By being alert we got quite a bit of gold; some of it was even in rather large nuggets. We kept getting into deeper water and the farther out we went the coarser were the gold particles. Nuggets, we began to call them. In four days' time back came our scouts. They reported rough country. Big cliffs and one waterfall above another. There was gold in small spots, but finer than that in the Jackpot bar. A half mile upstream there was a deep canyon with cliffs on each side. At the head of this canyon was the highest waterfall of all. It fell from about the same height as the sides of the canyon. That excited Etienne.

He clapped his hands and laughed aloud. 'Gentlemen, we have the solution. Let us go and look at this fall, but before we go let me tell you what we will see. At the foot of this fall there is a broad pool. It is almost round. The pool empties into the canyon over a circular bar of fairly big rocks holding back coarse gravel. The upper edge of the pool is back behind the cascade of falling water. The lower part of the cliff is sandstone. The falls drop over a ledge of hard rock. As the years pass the sandstone slowly crumbles and passes into the pool, and the finer parts go on with the water over the lip of that bar, that circular bar. Inside of that circle, we will find gold in big quantities. There will be nuggets, possibly as big as hens' eggs. The swirling water cannot drag them over the bar. The coarse gold in the Jackpot bar was fine enough to be carried out and downstream. I have told you the situation. Tell me, Ben, is that as you saw it?'

" 'Yes,' said Ben, 'that is the way it is. You could be right. But what a fortune awaits us there. Tell me, Etienne, how will we get it into our pouches?'

" 'Let's go look it over in the morning,' said Etienne.

"We did just that. We took a pick and a shovel and an ax to blaze trail. Etienne walked ahead. We kept on the rising ground beside the canyon on catching sight of the falls. Jackpot Falls, we already called it. There was the picture as Etienne had described it. Even at this height we could see the sandstone, as he had said, at the foot of the falls. We could see ten feet of it, and how much farther down it extended was anybody's guess.

"Was the gold there? One thing was sure. The coarse gold of the Jackpot did not come from over the falls, for no coarse gold was up there. But how to get it? Jeremiah looked at me, I looked at Jeremiah. It was not for nothing that I had brought five hundred feet of three-quarter inch rope. Good strong rope. Now I understood why fate had impelled me to bring it. I told the men what I had brought with me and said we could make a rope ladder and anchor it to the top of the cliff. Then we could, one at a time, climb down and make sure of the gold. If Etienne was correct there was an immense fortune awaiting us down there. We went back to camp and laid the rope out in parallel lines. But then we had to find one-and-a-half-inch saplings for rungs, cut them to proper length and fasten each end to the ropes. They must be spaced at nine-inch intervals. The ends must be made secure. That task took days. In the end, when it was finished, we loaded that rope on a sturdy ox and led it up our trail to a spot we had selected. We fastened the end to a giant tree near the cliff edge. Then we carefully let the other end down. Down it went and stopped at the water's edge at the rim of the pool. It looked firmly fastened at the top. Two hundred feet of ladder was fixed and ready. Who would descend to see if our hopes were to be realized?

"I had suggested it, so everyone felt I should make the first trial. So I got ready. I got a sack and put a two-gallon pail and a gold pan in it. I tied a shovel to my shoulders and slowly went down. At bottom I dipped the gold pan in a spot of gravel at pool's edge and began that circular motion. Yes, there was coarse gold. I emptied it into the pail. Then another panful. I kept up that washing and dipping until I had a two-gallon pail close to full of nearly pure gold nuggets. The weight surprised me. Leaving the pan and the shovel, I managed to climb back up. The others were eager to look at my pail.

" 'That's it,' Etienne said. 'Now let's send Jeremiah down and one of us will go back to camp with this and empty it into a deerskin. Then bring back two more pails and some pouches.'

"So that is how we did it. By day's end we had a real treasure of gold. That night we talked it over and decided it would be wise to take some short shakes up there to anchor the bottom of the ladder. By putting the shakes across the bottom rungs of the ladder and piling rocks on them, we had a fairly solid anchor to keep the ladder from swaying. Then we rigged a harness to hold a good load on our backs. By changing into the harness, each man could go down in his turn and bring up his take. It seemed best that two men should go down, and when a pail was full of the precious load, one man could take it up. Give the harness to the third man, who would then go down. By that time, the second man would be ready to climb out with his pailful. We did not burn up that ladder, but made good use of it. Our hopes kept rising and our treasure increasing. We did not go wild about our treasure, but we did work regular shifts.

"Etienne came up with another idea. If we took a gallon can and fastened a six-foot stick to it, we could reach down in the pool and come up with some real large nuggets, even mayhap as big as hens' eggs. So we made it up as he described and on the fourth day sent him down with it to try it out. By dipping three times he had the two-gallon pail full of nuggets after washing out the sand in the gold pan.

"The weather continued fine and our health remained good and our treasure increased. We kept tanning deerskins and making gold pouches. We were almost afraid to calculate the size of our fortune. We had decided to pool our entire take. We had $70,000 worth before we made the rope ladder. We could easily take out that much at Jackpot Falls in a week if the gold held out. And that it would seemed certain.

"Our garden was now giving us much fresh food. Also, we took a little time to gather wild berries. We took turns at getting venison so as to have enough meat. Our flour and cured hams and bacon still held out. These different foods no doubt were part of the reason we kept well and strong. All of us were from families who lived by the time-proved rules of health inherited from ancestors who had learned them centuries ago. Else, how could we live year after year without the aid of a doctor? The vinegar and honey drink was a factor in this. A medical doctor was far away should we get sick, and we did not intend to get sick. Etienne had lived for years away from any chance of getting a doctor's aid. The only way he could do that was by living a healthful life and eating the proper foods. Indeed, the rest of us were like him. I cannot remember needing attention of a doctor since childhood. Nor Jeremiah.

Nor Ben. Of course, the blessing of God, we acknowledged, was an important part of it.

"I had brought some chunks of comfrey root and planted them. Now we had several large comfrey clumps. We used some of those broad leaves in stews and the dried leaves to brew tea at least twice a week. Also, we had brought sassafras bark and used it for tea.

"About November 1 we took stock of our treasure. In spite of the fact that we didn't have absolutely pure gold, we weighed up what we had and decided we had over $400,000 worth. We kept at it two more days. The feeling that we had enough became stronger each day.

"One morning there were dark clouds rolling up from the west. Ben shook his head and said, 'Let us get away from here, fellows. We have enough. Who wants all the gold in the world? We already have more gold than we hoped to get when we came to this spot. Let us move on before we get into trouble.'

" 'Yes, Jeremiah chimmed in, 'I favor that idea. Let us get going back to where we came from. Gold is not everything. We hardly need $100,000 apiece. Any more might well prove a burden and not a help.'

"Etienne and I were of like mind. We each took one more turn at the foot of the ladder and then pulled it up and took it back to camp. We removed all trace of our work up at the top of that cliff. We checked over the wagons and the ox yokes. We hitched up the oxen and took a short trip to see if all was in working order.

"We put a false floor of shakes in one wagon and packed our gold under it. It was all in stout leather pouches, resting on deerskins and covered with more deerskins. Then we put the rope from the ladder on top of the shakes and dug our potatoes. When we got done with the garden, we had cabbage, carrots, squash, beets and onions. A fine sight it was, meaning that we believed we had aids to continued good health. Of course, Etienne knew how to get fresh green food even in the desert, but that would take time, and when we started home

63

we wanted to get there without undue delay. After getting in a stack of wood for the cabin, we took off up the ridges.

"That toilsome climb was much different from when we came down. Instead of a week, it took nearer three weeks to cover the same distance. Before we reached the crest, the storms caught up with us, but we made it over the pass and then had better going. We let the oxen take their time climbing up because they needed rest often, being soft after doing nothing but graze for five months. Now on the down passage we could go faster. Water was no problem till we left the mountains. On the Nevada plains, we could follow the Humbolt River.

"All along the way there were signs of the feverish passage of hundreds of wagons and pack trains. Broken-down wagons, goods tossed aside to lighten weight. The near approach to midwinter caused us to seriously consider our course. To plan on going east across the high plains in the dead of winter seemed to be daring fate. 'What do you think, Etienne?' I asked.

" 'I favor caution,' he said. 'I can guide this party to Salt Lake City, where we should be able to rent a house. At least we could get space to park our wagons. The main gold rush has passed through. There should be few "Gentiles" as they call us there. I suggest we try to spend the time till late March there. We have each held out a couple of gold pouches and they should be plenty to use to buy what we might need. I say, Salt Lake for us!'

"Ben nodded, Jeremiah nodded, I nodded. So we turned off in that direction the next day. On the desert in December there was dry grass for the oxen cured by the sun, and good food. We kept our canteens full of water and we even carried two large kegs of water from each waterhole. Etienne took us on a route most goldseekers never knew about. There was plenty of grass for the oxen. And he remembered enough waterholes to suffice.

"Etienne related, 'When I scouted for Fremont, we ranged over much of this area. We found water most people

64

know nothing about. It is fortunate that happened.'

"I thought about predestination and believed the whole affair of Etienne was foreordained.

"Some snow fell, but not enough to impede us. The oxen could still get plenty of grass. We slowly plodded along. Why hurry? We must wait out the winter somewhere. Why hurry to get to Salt Lake City and then pay for lodging or, at least, camping space.

"But we did get to Salt Lake City by Christmas time. And what a surprise met our eyes. Those hard-working Mormons had performed wonders. There were broad straight streets. They had built fine buildings for stores, a great temple, fine homes. They used stone, brick and wood. They had good masons, good carpenters and good brickmakers. They had made good use of every skill. In just over three years their industry had produced these wonderful streets lined with substantial buildings.

"We stopped at a wide place in the road on the outskirts of town. Soon a well-dressed man came along to greet us. His eyes roved over the fat ox teams. Eight good oxen. Four to the wagon. And four sturdy men and two riding horses. His eyes gleamed. Then he spoke to us. 'Welcome to this city, gentlemen. I am very glad to see you arrive. Most men in the past years have been going west. You seem bound east. If you will be pleased to stay over for four months I can find work for you and your oxen and a place to camp and plenty of wood and water and grass. My name is Jared Sparks.'

"We in turn named ourselves. David LaFollette, Etienne Ronald, Jeremiah LaFollette, and Ben Ferrin. 'Mr. Sparks, we are pleased to meet you. Show us how you can do what you said. Perhaps we can be useful to you and you to us. Please explain.'

'So Jared Sparks explained how the winter had caught them a bit short of firewood. He had a farm ten miles away where he raised hay, wheat and vegetables for his own use and also to sell. He said, 'There is timber in the hills at that farm. I also have a place in town where I sell farm products if I have some to spare. Also wood, but now I need men to cut wood and oxen to draw it into town where there is now ready sale. Are you interested? It seems to me that you men are disappointed miners on the way home. If you aid me, I will pay you well, say ten dollars a day for each man and two-fifty a day for each of the oxen and feed and food and lodging besides.'

"We replied, 'Mr. Sparks, you are partly right. We have been mining and are now on the way home to our homes. We have some gold, enough to pay our way. But we are not above working for wages if suitable employment is offered. Please show us where we can put our wagons and oxen tonight, and tomorrow three of us can go to the farm with you and see about the wood. Have you wagons to haul it?'

" 'Come along then and we will get settled in at my sales yard. There is feed and water. Then we can discuss our future plans.'

"In half an hour we were settled at his wood yard. There were two wagons there, one loaded with wood. Jared Sparks explained that he had two wagons at the farm with Brother Woods and two teams of oxen. He continued, 'We plan to bring in two loads of wood and then take the empty wagons back to the farm. Meanwhile, people drive here to buy wood or we deliver it if ordered delivered. This load is ordered, but I lack a team to make delivery. If you are pleased to, you can take this load to the buyer. I will direct you.'

"So Ben and Jeremiah put one team of oxen to the loaded wagon and made delivery while Etienne and I got things arranged at the camp. When Sparks got back he got Ben and Jeremiah and the four oxen comfortably placed for the night and then asked us all to eat the evening meal at his house. His family included four children. They were a bit shy.

" 'Gentlemen, meet my wife and children. Martha, this is Etienne Ronald, David LaFollette, Ben Ferrin and Jeremiah, David's brother. They will work for us with the wood. They will eat here tonight. Tomorrow, Etienne will stay with the covered wagons while the others will work in the woods.'

66

"Martha greeted us kindly, bade us sit. In a minute she called us all to the table where there was plenty of good food. Indeed, the Mormons took good care to have plenty of good though plain food. That was the same kind we were used to, and we were well pleased. The next day Jared rode with me and we got well acquainted. He explained that Brigham Young had decided that God in His providence had settled them in Utah to provide supplies to the gold seekers. And God had, so he thought, sent the gold seekers this way so their money would provide the Mormons with ready cash for purchases of such things as they needed. Therefore, the people here should treat us all fairly and encourage the passage to and fro of all well-behaved 'Gentiles,' as they called us. That made sense to me and I was certain that God had foreordained that the Mormons should take this course. I was very sure of it in our case. 'However,' Jared said, 'very few have come by headed east.'

"When we got to the farm he showed us two wagons loaded with wood. After putting our oxen in the barn to eat, he asked us to the house. There we found three children and the lady of the house. He said, 'Gentlemen, meet my wife. Nancy, this is David LaFollette and Ben Ferrin and Jeremiah, David's brother. They will help us with the wood and eat with us.'

"Nancy expressed pleasure at meeting us and we at meeting her and her children. In about a half hour along came two men with ox teams and sledges loaded with wood. Soon after, we were called to the table for the midday meal. This farm had large fields and big haystacks. There were pigs and chickens and milk cows. We had seen these things while we waited. We talked among ourselves about the two wives and concluded it was a common thing among the Mormons. At the table, we talked about the way to get the loaded wagons to Salt Lake City. Jared said that he thought our oxen were well able to take them in that afternoon, since they were sleek and strong from traveling at a leisurely pace. Jeremiah and I agreed that made good sense and, after eating, we hitched the oxen to the loaded wagons. Ben was to go to the woods and help cut more wood after they got the wood off the sledges onto the empty wagons we had brought.

"Jared again rode with me. Along the way he told me that among the Mormons it was common for a man to have two homes, two wives and two sets of children.

"He continued, 'Nancy is in charge out here when I am gone. Martha is in charge in town while I am gone. I try to spend half the time in each home. In summer I am really out on the farm more than half the time and in winter more than half my time is spent in town. Perhaps you did not notice, but we have a big cellar full of potatoes, cabbage, carrots and squashes. Also a granary with wheat and barley and oats. People come to buy every day. I do hope we will have enough to last our customers through the winter. And then we want to have a good supply for the gold seekers we expect to come along next summer.'

"'Mr. Sparks,' I said, 'it seems fortunate for you that you have got established here so well in three years' time. I know it is fortunate for our party.'

"'Fortunate?' he said. 'I say it was foreordained of God to be this way at this time.'

"'Mr. Sparks,' I replied, 'you may be correct. I, myself, am a believer in predestination. I am certain our coming here at this time is foreordained, as I believe the entire course of my life has been directed by God for my good and God's glory. In 1850 there were eighteen of us in two groups came west to wash gold. We came on horseback and did not touch Salt Lake City. Most of us prospered and four decided to stay and bought a farm. Eight of us bought a sailing ship and learned to sail it. We built buildings in San Francisco after getting tired of washing gold from the gravel. With the ship's captain's aid we learned to fish. We made two voyages with freight and two trips onto the open sea to catch fish before he thought us capable of sailing our ship to Panama, for we wished to get back to our families. This ship's captain had lost his crew to the mines, so he took up with us and taught us seamanship in return for a share of our gains. He was our captain on the voyage to Panama and bought the ship from us there to be able to carry gold seekers from there to Frisco. Then we were fortunate in getting a job helping with a pack train to Colón. Then we got a job on a ship to New Orleans. The fact is, our group of eight were able-bodied and willing. Total abstainers. And we agreed to stick together and keep regular watch as on board a ship. We moved against the main course of travel, and crewless ships were very glad to get our help. The captain took back the ship we eight had bought from him in Frisco. He had been left crewless and had sold willingly to us. We made a deal to keep him aboard and help him fish for shares of gain. Then, at Panama, he found he could take three hundred passengers to Frisco at a good price and bought the ship from us for $50,000. He made good money. In fact, he made that $50,000 from his share and the fare of the passengers he took to Frisco. So, we all prospered. Predestination is my name for what made our projects prosper. Now we are tired of sweating in the gravel beds and want to get back to our families and return to farming. The group of eight scattered last March, but this group is only four and I am the only one of that group of eight. But we dread crossing the plains in the dead of winter, so we took up your offer. We do not have to work for wages, for we have a small quantity of gold to pay expenses. However, we chose to work for good wages such as you offer. And we can see how you are doing well by hiring us.'

"Jared Sparks said he was well pleased, and as we moved along I told him of the fish we caught at Frisco and how we had built buildings without nails.

" 'Yes,' he said, 'we here have built many homes that way. In fact, our great temple is put together with wooden pegs.'

"Our oxen were active and inured to hard work. We got to the sales yard before dark and were able to make delivery of the wood to the anxious buyers. Then a good rest after a good meal.

"Out at the wagon, I told Etienne about Sparks' other family and the way the men brought the wood down from the hills. He suggested that I stay in Salt Lake City the next day; he would drive my team out to the farm. That suited me fine, as I had a curiosity to see more of the city and talk with people about what was being done.

"The next morning Jeremiah and Etienne set out at daylight. Soon after, Jared Sparks came by and suggested we take a walk through town. For one thing, he wished to engage more wood, seeing he had a bigger crew and would have plenty to sell. As we walked along, men would stop him and ask if he could spare a load or if he had spuds and other produce to spare. He had quite a list for most of the produce. He told them to come in that afternoon. About ten o'clock we came to a fine mansion. He knocked and went in. He came back out and asked me to come along. It was Brigham Young who met me at the door and bade me enter. Jared Sparks made us acquainted, and Young asked us to sit and be comfortable.

"We entered into a lengthy conversation. Mr. Young was much interested in learning of conditions in California and, as I had been there in 1850, 1851 and 1852, there was much I could tell him. He seemed to think that goldmining would not really be the thing for most men to undertake.

"I said, 'Mr. Young, many men have become wealthy by that means and many will no doubt succeed at it in years to come. However, there is getting to be much crime, robbery and murder. Our two groups in 1850 made a total of eighteen men. We were not boozers or gamblers. We got gold—yes, indeed, we got gold, but we put it into banks and sent much back to our families. Some bought their friends' claims and stayed on. Some sold out and took up other work, such as freighting or building homes and warehouses. Most of us drifted into such work and we did well. Perhaps never to become as rich as the most fortunate miners, but still we gathered a tidy sum. We traveled to San Francisco and looked over the country. We got time to sail the ship the eight of us purchased. We traded and sold fish. You must realize that miners had money, and that anyone with grain or meat to sell would take in a nice sum. Some decided to farm, and one group of five bought an old farm from a fine Spanish man whose son and help vanished into the gold fields. That is why he sold it. In the same way that is how we could buy the ship. We, a group of landlubbers, bought a good tight ship. Captain Burton was left helpless, but we bought him out and got him to stay on and teach us to work that ship. He showed us how to get fish and we went shares with him on that. He prospered and we prospered. Consider this: Fifteen men with fourteen horses came to town one morning. Before night we had bargained for Captain Burton's idle ship. We also got a job building a big warehouse without nails. You see, we knew how to build with wooden pegs. And we let two men go with the horses on a pack trip carrying supplies to a mining camp. The two jobs brought us $25,000 in four weeks' time. So it went. God had foreordained that we would get there just at the right time to do those tasks. Another four weeks saw us doing as well. Meanwhile, Captain Burton carefully trained us so as to go on voyages. First, freight jobs where we bought wheat and sold it in the mining area and doubled our costs. Burton came in for a share of that. Then two fishing trips, during which we did better financially than in trading. We did not have to wait for jobs. Jobs came to us. William Brannan, a wealthy man, watched us build without nails and wished he could get us to work for him. But somehow we had other projects.'

"Young broke in, 'Did you say William Brannan? He was here once but did not favor our project here and went to Frisco. How did he make out? Did he prosper?'

" 'Mr. Young,' I replied, 'that I cannot say, but while I was there last year he seemed to be wealthy and to associate with wealthy people.'

"Brigham Young went on to say, 'Mr. LaFollette, you have told an interesting story of life in the California gold fields and in San Francisco. You seem to have done well. I, myself, think that that frenzied prosperity is very apt to vanish as the morning fog. Then the workaday life of the sturdy farmer will prove the most desirable. I am much interested in what you said of building without nails.'

" 'Mr. Young, it might interest you to know that I was born in a log house that was build in 1826 in Indiana. My father used axes, augers and a hammer to build it with wood pegs. He later became wealthy as a famous breeder of fine horses and purebred cattle. My brother and I came from that home early this year. What you say about the life of a farmer is in accord with my present ideas. It was the idea the other seven had when we separated in St. Louis in February. But I was not yet persuaded. Now I am certain that farming is, at least for me, the best life. For my brother Jeremiah it is what he chooses. While we have a little gold we crave to live the life of the self-sufficient farmer and are on the way east to embark on that career. As I said, there was not a nail in my birthplace nor a saw mark anywhere. The door was put together with pegs and is still in use. We are comfortable there.'

"Mr. Young asked us to take the midday meal with him and kept talking about my ideas. He said, 'I am convinced that it was foreordained that we should settle here and build a city and grow crops to feed the passing hordes of gold seekers. I am making sure that they get good treatment here and we will at all times deal fairly with them. They will furnish us with cash with which we can buy what is needed from outside, and we will sell them food to help them on their way.'

" 'Mr. Young,' I said, 'glad I am to hear your plans. I too believe it was foreordained that you settle here and take the attitude you do. I am a Baptist. We call ourselves the Primitive Predestinarian Baptists. If it was not foreordained, then tell me why Mr. Sparks came to us to hire us and our oxen to help him with the wood business. We had hardly paused when he approached us and made us a fair offer. We brought in two loads yesterday and will do it again today if it is out there ready to haul. And the demand is keen, as I realized when watching him take orders this morning. But I wonder about a deep snow. Have you sleds here capable of hauling big loads of wood? If it does snow, you may be sure much wood will be needed.'

" 'That makes me think,' Young rejoined. 'Yes, I believe it was foreordained that your party should come when you did. And that you should ask about sleds. That is something we must prepare before snow comes and finds us unprepared. Yes, it must have been foreordained.'

" 'About predestination,' I said. 'I am reminded of a thing that happened to one of our pastors. He was going on horseback from one appointment to another. He taught music, and even common school at times, and the effect his preaching and that of other elders was being felt. One day on the road a ruffian met him and berated him for preaching predestination. He threatened the good elder's life, saying anyone who taught predestination should be killed. 'I have a mind to drag you from your horse and beat you to death,' he said as he grabbed hold of the bridle with great oaths issuing from his lips. The good elder asked him if he claimed it was wrong to say what is to be, will be.

" 'Do you claim that what is to be, won't be, my friend?' asked the elder. 'I would like to debate that subject with you any time before a large audience. I believe that what is to be, will be.' The man cursed some more and declared his intention to drag the elder from his horse and beat him to death right then.

"But Elder Thompson replied, 'God uses the wrath of men to praise Him. And He will restrain the remainder of wrath.'

"In spite of even more dire threats, that ruffian finally released his hold on the bridle reins and Elder Thompson went on his way to preach to thousands over the years till he reached a good old age. I hold to the same doctrine. What is to be, will be.

"I really do not know why I told Brigham Young all the foregoing. Perhaps it was because the talk had awakened in my mind vivid memories of my childhood in Indiana and the friendly conversation impelled me to express my deepest feelings. And then the long procession of foreordained happenings of the past four years must have led me to relate so much of my experiences and my inmost thoughts.

"After the meal, Jared Sparks took his leave, for he had more business to attend to. But Mr. Young wished me to stay, since I had made an unusual impression on him and he wished to get a better idea of me and my life and beliefs. After more talk of conditions in California, he suggested we walk about the city. He wished to show me the way the city had grown and how the hard-working Mormons planned to further improve the area.

"They had already constructed irrigation ditches to water their farms, and they had brick kilns and stone quarries and sawmills. He took me by some of their chief buildings and even to view their temple. The temple was magnificent. And all without a nail. He did not invite me inside the temple. I later learned that no Gentile could enter that building. Then we separated after he had thanked me for telling him so much about California. As we parted he said again that they planned to be helpful to all passing gold seekers and to give them honest service.

"I went back to the covered wagons. We slept in them, as we had during our journey over the great stretch of vacant land on the way to Salt Lake City. Etienne and Jeremiah had gotten back in good time and were able to make delivery on the same day. I asked about Ben Ferrin, and Jeremiah said he was feeling fine. Then Etienne told of how he had enjoyed the trip. But we talked it over and decided that when Sunday came we would not work. The oxen would need the rest and so would we. We decided that Ben could change off to drive oxen a while if he wished. We thought it best that, with three working, we manage it so as to let each man take a turn at the camp wagons and lighten the monotony. If we kept up this manner of working, we ought to be able to get through the next three months in good health and spirits. The third day I took Jeremiah's team and talked to Ben Ferrin at noon. He was ready to drive in if I would take his place in the woods. Then he stayed at the covered wagons the fourth day. The fifth day was Saturday, and we held to our steady work. But on Monday Jeremiah said that, if we pleased, he would stick to driving oxen except for one day a week when he would like to stay in town. Sunday we were all in town, except Ben Ferrin who was out at the farm. Then Etienne drove out and took his turn at the work in the woods.

"Soon we got into a regular routine, except that Jeremiah kept to the oxen and Ben and I were generally the ones in the woods. That suited us fine, because we grew up in the woods at home. Sparks kept his woods crew at the job steady, except for Sundays.

"The weather stayed fine. Only a few showers over the months we were in Salt Lake City, and never over two inches of quick-melting snow. We were quite accustomed to the work. Sparks fed the oxen the best hay and a good amount of corn. He wanted to keep them in good flesh. He really needed their help. He gave us the very best of plain food. He needed us too. One thing I noted was that they saved even the small tree limbs. These they used in the farm stoves. They explained that many farms had no timber and had to use sagebrush. This they gathered in great heaps, and in cold spells it was a tedious task to keep a fire going with such fuel. But those people meant to succeed and were willing to accept such conditions if that was their lot.

"We talked among ourselves about Sparks' two households, and after further investigation, we found quite a few Mormon men had four or five wives and as many households. They would scrupulously divide their time between the different wives as near equally as convenient. The women accepted that arrangement believing that they gained immortal standing thereby. Indeed, I heard that Brigham Young possessed thirteen wives.

"These things did not seem really proper. However, we knew that over much of the world, especially among the Chinese and Mohammedans, many wives were the accepted thing, though four was the legal number with the latter. We Baptists held to the thought that one wife was all any man was entitled to. As, indeed, was the case throughout the civilized world. When we realize that there are about the same number of women as men, it would seem that monogamy would appear to be just.

"We were merely passing the time, but we were glad to have jobs at good wages. To be sure, only three of us were working at any one time, but Sparks reckoned that made for more productive workmen.

"The time passed by. The days became longer, one hour each month, and by April 10 we thought it time to be on our way. Grass was springing up in the hills, and even on the high plains last year's grass was nutritious. So we cast up our accounts and Sparks paid us what was remaining of our wages. Five hundred and sixty-five dollars for less than four months' work in winter was more than the income to be expected in most parts of the United States at that time. And when we realized that we had had our food besides, it struck us that our situation was very satisfactory.

"We bade Jared Sparks and his two families farewell, paid a last call on Brigham Young, and rolled away the next morning. We were glad that each day we were getting nearer to our families. In truth, Jeremiah was not married. Neither was Etienne Ronald. Yet they had kinfolk or good friends. Etienne proved that when he met up with old cronies at Fort Bridger. Again, as the days passed at the trading post where I first laid eyes on him, there were old friends to greet him and spend hours in relating their adventures since last they met. The rest of us listened in and did not realize that we were hearing the history of a time that was past. But so it was. And with us, our course of life would be much different in 1853 and the years following. There was much talk of railroads, of slavery, of manifest destiny. These things stirred the nation. Etienne knew that the trapper had gotten most of the beaver. It was true that the buffalo still moved in great herds, but he had had enough of the life on the plains.

"Etienne announced that he would go on to St. Louis and settle down. The plains had changed and he had changed too. So indeed had we. We would never be, in the next three years, the same as we had been during the past three years.

76

But the gold rush still persisted. Already trail caravans had reached this spot. As we went east they went west. Would they win, though? Would they be as fortunate as we had been, or would their graves dot the western plains?

"Some would and some would not.

"So it is always. The fate of each individual is in the hands of the Almighty. Through struggle and through sturdy labor His purpose will be served.

"We pressed on to St. Louis. There we divided the gold. Etienne, Ben and I had each gained nearly $175,000 in the space of less than four years. Jeremiah had a bit over $100,000. These were big sums for common people in those days. As Jeremiah and I moved on toward our old home, our thoughts reached ahead to those loved ones there. We longed to hold them in our embrace. We discounted the struggles and the trials of the past in our joyous anticipation of the future.

"Mr. Ephraim, this has been a long story. I have given details of many things because I thought you might be interested in hearing how we in that time long past met and overcame our problems.

"Now in the next few years Jeremiah drove his wagon to western Missouri and had a farm and orchard. At one time he had two thousand trees in that orchard. The market for his fruit and produce was in St. Joseph. He married and reared a large family.

"As for myself, I brought my family west to California and farmed for a time. Then we moved to the Willamette Valley of Oregon. As my children grew up and married I was able to give each a respectable farm and a cash start. My wife passed away many years ago. I married again. My second wife passed away and I now have a third wife.

"You may wonder that I am here washing gold again. But it is simple. We have a good farm and we raise good crops. But in these times of business stagnation there is little call for farm crops. So to get ready cash here I am washing gold again. Gold is always in demand. So it has been in the past, and so it will be in the future.

"I have often wondered if anyone else ever stumbled over

77

the Jackpot. Did that bend fill up again with gold-bearing gravel? Perhaps some big company moved in a dredge and worked all the way up to Jackpot Falls and even into the cliff past the falls. If so, they must have gotten out millions of dollars' worth of the shiny metal.

"Then, again, perhaps no man in all this time has found his way to that bonanza. If so, there is a big fortune in gold awaiting the man fortunate enough to find that spot. If he does, he will find our cabin and the plow I left there.

"Mr. Ephraim, I have finished the story. It is late. Let us rest. Tomorrow we must get going again to get out some gold to bolster our finances in this time of stagnant business conditions.

The blacksmith yawned and said, "Mr Jones, this second-hand story is ended. You expressed a desire to hear it, so I have combed the recesses of my memory to get most of the things David LaFollette told me. It interested me then, it interests me now, and I believe it interests you.

"Mr. Ephraim," I said, "David LaFollette was my great uncle. My grandfather, his younger brother, became wealthy breeding fine horses and purebred shorthorn cattle. He came west in 1894 and visited David. He visited many others of his kin and took notes of their family history. After trips to Missouri and Indiana, he put together the knowledge he had collected into a small book. I have a copy of that book. A picture of David LaFollette is in that book. Of course, I was interested in that story."